OXFORDSHIRE MILLS

OXFORDSHIRE MILLS

Wilfred Foreman

PHILLIMORE

1983

Published by
PHILLIMORE & CO. LTD.
Shopwyke Hall, Chichester, Sussex

ISBN 0 85033 441 1

Printed and bound in Great Britain by
THE CAMELOT PRESS LTD.
Southampton, Hants.

CONTENTS

LIST OF PLATES

(between pages 8 and 9)

ACKNOWLEDGEMENTS

I would like to acknowledge with gratitude the permission of the following for the use of their photographs in this book:

Oxford City Library, Plates 2, 4, 8, 12, 14, 16, 24, 27, 31, 32, 65; Museum of the History of Science, Oxford, Plates 23, 33, 41, 42, 44, 56, 58, 62, 64; *Oxford Mail and Times*, Plate 22; Mr. Brice Witney, Plate 50; Museum of Rural Life, Reading, Plate 67.

LIST OF TEXT FIGURES

To my family

INTRODUCTION

IN 1969 WHEN I WAS DOING occasional building survey work for the Oxford City and County Museum I was asked to investigate a tumbledown building at Barford St Michael, by the River Swere. I had always been interested in Industrial Archaeology and when I found myself in a little building full of meshing gears I was completely fascinated. I figured out that it must have been a water-mill, and from that moment of revelation was born my interest (my family might well say my obsession) in mills.

On that first visit a sensible person might well have gone home, for there was no roof covering, no floor boards, and it was snowing—it was sheer chance, too, that the first mill I had ever examined was the only one in the county to which access was freely available at that time.

My map showed that the immediate area was rich in mill sites which I began to investigate systematically, quickly explaining myself lest I be viewed with the same suspicion as the officials who were investigating the several possible routes of a major link road.

I realised that I should have paid more attention to those mills which were still working when I was a lad. I often went to Enslow Mills (Bletchington) to get bran for my rabbit; then my main concern was whether Bill Savins would serve me, for he had the biggest hands of any man I knew, and bran was measured by the handful. I can recall the loud humming noises akin to another sound I knew, the threshing machine, but if I had been daring enough to enter to see what was happening I don't doubt that I would have been chased out—a condition then to be accepted between adults and small boys.

By chance I was made aware of the Wind and Water Mill section of the Society for the Protection of Ancient Buildings and I suddenly found myself with a host of people who had a common interest—mills. Such people suffer the generic title of 'molinologist', the sort of word beloved by quizmasters, but I find it so unwieldy I hope that it will not appear again. Among S.P.A.B. literature I found gazetteers compiled some ten years earlier listing the mills of many counties, but Oxfordshire had been ignored; indeed, it would seem that we were of no account at all as far as mills went.

I set out to remedy this intolerable situation, investigating and listing all possible sites and making scale drawings of whatever mill machinery there was or could be seen to have existed. There is a book of my drawings available from the S.P.A.B. Though trained as an architect I did not attempt building surveys, merely indicating the plans and sections, for I consider the whole essence of a mill to be the machinery in it. This county had a fine tradition of masons' work, but 'commercial' would best describe the standard of construction of the carcase of the mill buildings, few having coursed masonry or well-worked quoins, the timber-framing in the roof is disappointing, and it can be recognised that some were roofed with thatch—aligned with labourers' cottages and lesser farm buildings.

At first I thought my research was for my benefit alone and I did not make careful notes of documentary sources; now I have been encouraged to produce this book I hope that true historians will not be too critical of me for the lack.

Both the County Museum Services and the Map Room of the Bodleian Library have provided invaluable help; the Science Museum Library in London has afforded me access to the Simmons' papers; moreover I owe particular thanks to Wendy Barnes of the County Record Office and to Malcolm Graham, local historian at the Oxford City Library. My thanks are due for permission to use material gathered from all those sources. I owe thanks, too, to county historian Ralph Mann who helped me in the Chipping Norton area; to Jasmine Howse for information on north Berkshire; and to Eric Cooper, who did some of the photographic work.

Above all I must thank Kenneth Major who was kind enough to read my MS. in it's final form; it has been much enhanced by his suggestions, and by the improvements and corrections he made.

Presumably this will be an introduction to mills for some so I must write of basic things. To those who have read all the recognised books I make no apology, for I have gleaned facts from many new sources, maybe not especially applicable to Oxfordshire, but meat and drink to the confirmed m........t.

I must thank my hosts for inviting me into their mill premises; but if this book suggests a cart blanche invitation to visit I must point out that most mills are privately owned and many are dwellings. Just one is in County Council ownership (Charney Bassett) and hopefully it will soon be open to the public as a mill museum. The mills at Ardington and West Hendred are craft workshops and I am sure they won't chase you away. Venn Mill is now in enthusiastic private hands undergoing restoration, and callers are welcomed, while after recent restoration work Mapledurham Mill is now open to visitors.

If anyone becomes sufficiently encouraged by this book to join the Wind and Water Mill section of the Society for the Protection of Ancient Buildings, the address is 55 Great Ormond Street, London, WC1N 3JA. Besides fostering an interest in mills they offer a comprehensive list of mill literature, including a gazetteer of all mills open to visitors. The International Molinological Society caters for those who wish to become more deeply involved (2 Eldon Road, Reading, RG1 4DH), while The Midland Wind and Water Mills Group

(5 The Crescent, Bromsgrove, Worcs., B60 2DQ) might be considered to cover north Oxfordshire.

Even more localised there are three organisations seeking members: Wheatley Wind Mill is in the process of restoration by volunteer help; at Combe Mill you can help run an 1852 beam engine, do smithing, conserve rural artefacts; at Charney Bassett Mill restoration work is being done by the Wantage Industrial Archaeology Group.

To use the gazetteers to best advantage you will need the relevant Ordnance Survey maps; of the older maps to be studied Richard Davis's map (1793) has been reprinted at a modest price, as has Roque's map of Berkshire (1761). Robert Plott's map (1675) is available, on which a few wind-mills are indicated; and Bryant's map (1823) is available in the County Record Office and in the History Section of Oxford City Library. Ogilby's series of maps of the coach routes of England (1675) will reveal much if you can get your hands on a copy; in the Oxford City Library they have an exclusive copy of a county map made by Phil Overton in 1715.

If your parish records are available study them with care, and if you find any special information please share it with this surveyor, who is not a very good historian.

WILFRED FOREMAN

59 Lake Street,
Oxford, OX1 4RR

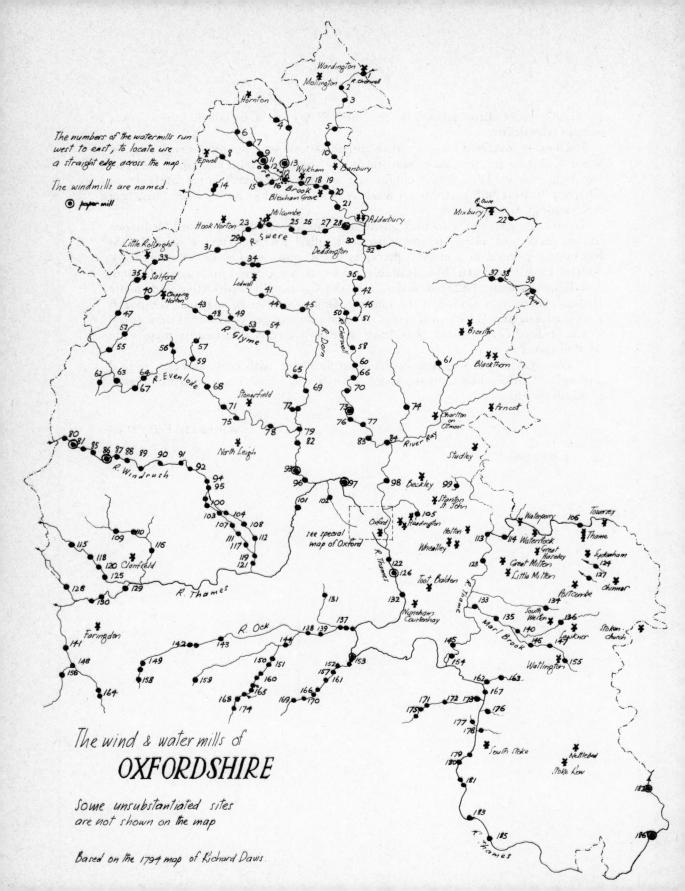

The numbers of the watermills run
west to east, to locate use
a straight edge across the map.

The windmills are named.

⊙ paper mill

The wind & water mills of

OXFORDSHIRE

Some unsubstantiated sites
are not shown on the map

Based on the 1794 map of Richard Davis.

Chapter One

BACKGROUND HISTORY

THE NEED for a milling process was established as soon as man decided to make his life pleasanter by supplementing his hard-won carnivorous diet with grains and cereals. The chance crushing of grains between two lumps of stone would have developed into the more convenient rolling of a stone cylinder on a smooth stone base, or a circular hollowed-out stone base which accepted a rotating convex-faced upper stone, working one-handed, the user squatting on the ground. Later larger versions would have been pushed round by a standing person, or pulled round by a small animal.

Such arrangements have persisted through centuries and can be found in use today in those countries we like to call under-developed.

In Britain the round type was called a *quern*. Despite its harsh suppression in manorial times, and the adoption of power milling, the quern continued in use in England; 16th- and 17th-century wills proved in this county show them to be as highly valued as anything among the family possessions. They are usually described as barley querns, which sounds as if they played their part in the brewing of the family beer.

There is much speculation on man's awareness of the properties of the wheel as a means of progression, and just as much about the first application as a means of gaining power from moving water—eventually someone recognised that the rotating wheel could be applied to turn those irksome querns.

No records exist until about 100 B.C., when both the Greeks and Romans wrote of water-power in use for grinding grain. The use of the waterwheel was not known in the Americas, the African continent, or Australasia until the settlers of modern history penetrated those areas. Because the Romans knew all about water-powered milling it is easy to assume that they brought that knowledge to Britain, but so far excavations have not revealed that there was widespread use. In this county there is a tantalising excavation of a Roman villa near North Leigh, beautifully sited within a loop of the River Evenlode, but no evidence of a mill. The Romans did use querns. After the Romans left Britain there was a period of some centuries in which their elaborate settlements and buildings fell into decay, when areas that had been drained and

1

developed reverted to marshland, and when any corn-mills which might have been built could have disappeared completely.

Then came the Saxons. In this county they spread over the river valleys; they drained marshy areas by channelling, and on those channels they established their simple mills, the mills that eventually were recorded by William the Conqueror's minions in 1086. The formidable Domesday List then compiled covered the major part of England and was a register of those properties that owed dues to the new king. The List is particularly detailed in Oxfordshire and I have extracted the 200 mill sites listed, sites which are recognised as being in the immediate area of those mill sites listed in the modern gazetteer. (When attempting to trace parochial sites remember that some parishes were once much larger and have been sub-divided, parish boundaries have changed, and there appear such anomalies as mills listed in Cowley and Headington parishes actually being on the River Cherwell and apparently belonging to Oxford city.)

'A mill' was one pair of stones driven by one waterwheel and where a parish seems to have some untraceable sites it may be that there was more than one mill under one roof. Some of the sites may have been animal powered; Aelfric, Abbott of Eynsham, writing of the things he saw happening locally somewhat before the Norman invasion, described both water-mills and animal-powered mills in use. You will see some mills have a value assessed in eels; they were always caught in large numbers in the trash grids which protected the water-wheels from floating debris (or even wicker eel traps). One wonders why those mills were particularly chosen.

THE DOMESDAY LIST

Saxon Name	Mills	Assessment	Present Name
Advelle	1	6s.	Adwell
Bensentone	2	40s.	Benson
Bentone	4	25s.	Steeple Barton
Blochesham	6	56s. 4d.	Bloxham
Banesberie	1	8s.	Banbury
	1	5s. 4d.	Banbury
	3	45s.	Banbury
Britewell	1	20d.	Brightwell Baldwin
Bladon	2	14s.	Bladon
		125 eels	
Bertone	1	2s.	Barton
	2	10s.	Barton
Bureford	2	25s.	Burford
Bereford	1	9s.	Barford (Cheney)
Bernecestre	2	40s.	Bicester
Brohtone	2	16s,	Broughton

The Domesday List—*cont.*

Saxon Name	Mills	Assessment	Present Name
Bortone	1	4s.	Black Bourton
	1	3s.	Black Bourton
Bradewelle	2	20s.	Broadwell
Brotone	2	12s. 6d.	Broughton Pogges
Blecestone	1	7s. 6d.	Bletchington
Birtone	1	3s.	Wescot Barton
Bristelmestone	1	11s.	Brighthampton
Cornewell	1	2s.	Cornwell
Chidentone	part	20d.	Kiddington
	1	5s.	Over Kiddington
Circendene	3	12s.	Sarsden
Cote	1	2s.	Nethercote (Lewknor)
Celgrave	5	60s.	Chalgrove
Cestretone	1	10s.	Chesterton
Cuchesam	3	18s.	Cuxham
Couelie	1	40s.	Cowley
	1	35s.	Cowley
Caningham	1	44d.	Kingham
Cerselle	2	20s.	Churchill
Caversham	1	20s.	Caversham
Craymeres	2	40s.	Crowmarsh
Celford	1	3s. 4d.	Old Chalford
Chadelintone	1	30s.	Kidlington
Cherielentone	2	35s.	Kirtlington
Cropelie	2	28s.	Cropnedy
	1	7s. 4d.	Cropnedy
Cube	1	3s.	Combe
Coges	1	10s.	Cogges
Cersetone	1	15s. 6d.	Cassington
		75 eels	
Chestitone	1	50d.	Chastleton
Codesdone	1	12s.	Cuddesdon
Dorchestre	1	20s.	Dorchester
	4	38s.	Dorchester
Dadintone	3	41s.	Deddington
		100 eels	
Dene	2	5s.	Dene
Draitone	1	10s.	Drayton
Dochelintone	1	12s.	Ducklington
Draitone	1	4s.	Drayton (Banbury)
Esthale	2	27s.	Asthall
Estone	1	30s.	North Aston
Edrote	1	5s.	Heythrop
Eglesham		12s.	Eynsham
		450 eels	Enysham
Etone	1	15s.	Water Eaton

The Domesday List—*cont.*

Saxon Name	Mills	Assessment	Present Name
Esthcote	1	5s.	Ascot D'Oiley
Edburgberie	2	30s.	Adderbury
Feringford	2	10s.	Fringford
Fuelwelle	1	10s.	Fullwell
Fylebroc	1	10s.	Fullbrook
Godentone	1	3s.	Godington
Gadintone	1	11s.	Gatehampton
Garinges	1	20s.	Goring
Hedentone	2	50s.	Headington
Horton	2	6s. 8d.	Worton
Henestan	4	19s.	Church Enstone
Hornelie	part	16d.	Horley
Hochenartone	2	20s.	Hook Norton
Haiford	1	12s.	Upper Heyford
Hidrecote	1	11s.	Gatehampton
Hegford	1	10s.	Lower Heyford
Haneberge	1	10s.	Handborough
Hantone	1	15s.	Hampton Poyle
Hansitone	1	5s.	Hensington
Langefort	2	20s.	Langford
Lineham	1	7s. 6d.	Lyneham
Letelade	1	20s.	Islip
Lavachanole	1	20d.	Lewknor
Lachebroc	site	10s.	Lashbrook
Lege	1	12s. 8d.	North Leigh
Misseberie	2	9s. 4d.	Mixbury
Mongewel	2	45s.	Mongewell
Minstre	1	10s.	Minster Lovell
	2	20s.	Minster Lovell
	2	40s.	Minster Lovell
Midelcube	part	2s.	Milcombe
	part	2s.	Milcombe
Malpedreham	1	20s.	Mapledurham
Middeltone	½	15s.	Great Milton
Niwetone	½	25d.	South Newington
	½	16d.	South Newington
Neyham	1	20s.	Nuneham Courtney
Nortone	3	62d.	Chipping Norton
Optone	2	10s. 4d.	Wooton
Oxenforde	1	10s.	Oxford
	1	40s.	Oxford
	1	40s.	Oxford
Peritone	1	5s.	Pyrton
Redrefeld	1	20s.	Rotherfield Greys
Radeford	1	20d.	Radford
Rowesham	part of 2	11s. 6d.	Rowsham

The Domesday List—*cont.*

Saxon Name	Mills	Assessment	Present Name
Sciptone	6	55s.	Shipton under Wychwood
Stoch	1	9s. 5d.	Waterstock
Stantone	3	40s.	Stanton Harcourt
Sumertone	1	20s. 400 eels	Somerton
Sanford	1	30d.	Sandford St. Martin
Surford	1	6s.	Swerford
Salford	part	12d.	Salford
Senendene	—	—	Shennington
Stoches	2	20s.	North Stoke
Tame	1	20s.	Thame
Tademertone	1	4s.	Tadmarton
	1	5s.	Tadmarton
Tachelie	1	10s.	Tackley
Teightone	2	32s. 6d. 62s. 6d. and eels	Taynton
Trop	1	6s. 125 eels	Thrup
Wigentone	1	8s.	Wiggington
Wistele	1	8s.	Whitehill
Witecerce	1	20s.	Whitchurch
Werochestan	1	8s.	Wroxton
Westone	2	4s.	South Weston
Watelintone	2	10s. 8d.	Watlington
Westone	2	4s.	Weston on the Green
Witenie	2	32s. 6d.	Witney
Wicham	1	30s.	Wykham

When the county boundary changes took place in 1974 part of north Berkshire was brought into the enlarged Oxfordshire. I think of my mill survey as being within the old boundaries though I cannot ignore the new. I have visited all the mill sites we 'acquired' from Berkshire and done some document research in the County Record Office at Reading. The parochial pattern was much the same as in Oxfordshire; fulling mills serviced a lively cloth industry and there was some paper-making done.

Of the 86 Berkshire parishes involved only 46 of them had mills which owed dues; later dates noted are for interest.

Saxon Name	Mills and Assessments	Present Name
Apleford	2 at 25s.	Appleford
Ardingtone	1 at 11s., 1 at 25s.	Ardington
Bedretone	1 at 5s.	Betterton

Mills in Berkshire Parishes—*cont.*

Saxon Name	Mills and Assessments	Present Name
Bertune	2 at 40s.	Barton
Blithberie	1 at 30d., 1 at 4s.	Blewbury
Bocheland	1 at 12s. 6d.	Buckland
Bristowelle	1 at 20s.	Brightwell
Celsei	3 at 62s.	Cholsey
Cenrea	1 at 4s., 1 at 50s., 1 at 2s.	Childrey
Cerletone	1 at 5s., 1 at 7s. 6d., part 5s.	Charlton
Cernei	noted in 12th century and 1594	Charney
Cocheswelle	noted in 1436 s/e boundary	Coxwell
Coleselle	3 separate one-thirds, 10s. each	Coleshill
Comenore	2 at 50s.	Cumnor
Dudochesforde	1 at 5s.	Duxford
Edtone	noted in 1333 and 1540	Eaton
Eissesberie	1 at 10s.	Ashbury
Ferendone	1 at 35s.	Faringdon
Fivehide	noted in 1427	Fyfield
Gainz	1 at 6s. 6d.	Ginge
Hachborne	1 at 12s.	W. Hagbourne
Hanlei	1 at 12s. 6d., 2 at 30s.	W. Hanney
Hannei	2 at 27s. 6d., 2 at 12s. 6d.	E. Hanney
Harwelle	1 at 30d.	Harwell
Henret	east mill 20s., west mill 10s., east fulling mill noted 1759	Hendred (Ginge)
Lachinge	1 at 30d.	E. Lockinge
Ledecumbe	2 at £3	Letcombe Bassett
Ledencumbe	5 at £4	Letcombe Regis
Merceham	a second mill noted in 1135	Marcham
Middletune	1 at 12s. 6d., 1 at 10s.	Milton
Moretone	1 at 12s. 6d.	N. Morton
	1 at 12s. 6d.	S. Morton
Oluricestone	2 at 12s. 6d.	Woolstone
Ordai	1 at 12s.	Littleworth
Serengeford	1 at 30d., 1 at 5s., 150 eels	Shillingford
Seriveham	2 at 20s.	Shrivenham
Sevacoord	2 corn, 2 fulling, 12th century	Seacourt
Sotwelle	1 at 15s.	Sotwell
Spersholt	1 at 5s.	Sparsholt
Stanford	2 at 7s. 8d.	Stanford in the Vale
Stivetune	3 at 45s.	Steventon
Sudtune	2 windmills, 1 fulling, 1419, 1 in 1458, 2 in 1608, 2 burned down 1756	Sutton Wick
Sudtune	3 at 50s.	Sutton Courtney
Wachensfeld	1 at 25s.	Watchfield
Wanetinz	1 at 100d., 1 at 6s. 3d., 1 at 15s., 1 at 30s.	Wantage
Wareford	1 at 7s. 6d.	Garford
Witeham	1 at 10s.	the Wittenhams

The first book on the history of milling was published in four volumes in 1898 (Bennett and Elton) and is not readily available nowadays. With the steady production of milling books since Bennett and Elton it might be thought that everything to be said has been said, yet Oxfordshire mills have been ignored and unchronicled. The very familiarity of the local mill made it so common-place that no-one bothered to record it, nor can the printed word explain how to acquire the sensitivities of listening, sniffing, and feeling, all special to the miller. True, he did not go unnoticed by poets and songsters, who show him as a jolly, brawling, grasping, gay, villainous, jovial unscrupulous rogue, with a mention of the click-clack of the mill, and the kingfisher o'er the pond, but never a suggestion that he was the man who contrived, improved, and maintained machinery which was for centuries more complex than anything else in the community.

The first county directories available date from the early 1830s, but they are not at all helpful; it is much later in the century that the working millers are properly indicated, rather late in the day to be informative.

The miller had no doubt always been considered a little superior to the general run of village labour, a tradesman to be admired along with the blacksmith and carpenter, but suddenly there was less dignity in his calling. The Central European wheat-growing areas started producing and exporting a much finer, whiter flour, prepared between closely-set rollers and carefully sifted. It would have appealed to the newly-prosperous townees, and millers found themselves supplying a diminishing list of customers. No doubt the small village millers in this county were better off than most, still finding work for their mills in processing cereals to provide animal food for the farmers, filling in between whiles grinding the small parcels of grain grown by the cottagers on their gardens and allotments.

We are told that general labourers subsisted on a diet of oatmeal, but oats were not processed in the local mills—the perforated tiles found hereabouts were for malting kilns, not oat kilns.

Robert Early's recent books on the Witney wool trade tell of the boring (but substantial) oatmeal diet of the wool workers; the wool wagons returning to Witney after delivering blankets to the ports would be the obvious way to bring back supplies from the oat-growing areas. Those wagons specially built for the wool trade are a reminder of those built for millers—there are memories of them being smarter and less heavily-built than farm wagons, but the only photograph I have is of the wagon from Somerton mill which is not very distinct. At Lower Tadmarton Mill (now a residence) they have a set of bells which was part of the horses's harness, so it would seem that the mill equipage might have been rather special.

The real failure of the country mills was brought about by the new products of the industrial revolution. Portable steam engines became available to farmers, besides smaller units fuelled by petrol and oil, and with these the farmer was now able to do one-time mill work right on the farm, using the new portable grinding and crushing machinery also available. Even gleaning, the one-time cottager's standby for bonus supplies of grain, was no longer worthwhile because of the efficiency of the new reapers.

At the beginning of World War I many of our mills were no longer working, or were dragging along with little hope. The need to process foodstuffs which could not be imported did bring a few mills back into use, but by and large their worn out, obsolete millwork was so inefficient that the outraged Minister of Food would not risk any of his precious grain with them. After the war small mills never had a hope of getting back into operation, while those that had struggled through found that their out-dated equipment could no longer compete with the well-established town mills.

Some of the slightly larger mills—I can think of Bletchington and Cassington —had been equipped for roller milling and the bleaching and super sifting associated with the 'whiter than white' flour, but they could not compete against the large port-established 'factories'. Bletchington was sold up in 1928 and Cassington ceased a few years later; the mill gear was sold as scrap in 1970. Even had they had the man-power our last few mills would have found it difficult to meet the stringent standards expected in World War II. Moreover, the layout of the mills was ill-suited to cope with the new 'safety at work' standards which had become law. Some just managed to keep in production processing animal foods, some were directed to small factory work, and the metal parts of the idle mill machinery were likely to be plundered for that noble cause, the War Effort.

Fringford Mill was recently restored to working condition; otherwise it is sad to think that there is not another mill in the county in working condition. Nowadays there is a problem in the lack of a working supply of water, a problem which will not lessen; indeed it will get worse as we make greater demands on water resources for domestic and commercial use.

I hope Berkshire will not mind if I now claim Wantage Mill in the Oxfordshire list—the only mill which has never stopped producing domestic flour.

1. Taynton Mill gear was dismantled in 1978 and is stored elsewhere. Note the well-worn steps.

The Mill. Adderbury. Oxon.
18

2. Adderbury Mill buildings still exist as a private house.

3. Adderbury Grounds Mill from the tail, taken in 1981. The mill is complete but the head pond is lost.

4. Botley Mill in the late 19th century. Only the waterways remain.

5. Artifacts displayed at Abbey Mills, Abingdon. The waterwheel is still in place inside the restaurant which now occupies the site.

6. The foot of the stone crane just shows alongside a newly-dressed bedstone at Castle Mills, taken *c.* 1900.

7. Plenty of water at the site of Castle Mills, with St George's Tower on the right. There is evidence of a man-powered windlass on the ground floor of the tower which operated a water pump in the basement.

8. Bodicote Mill when it had a dust problem in 1900.

9. Chalgrove in 1978. The front gable was rebuilt in 1870 and the right-hand roof was thatched.

10. Cutt Mill in 1978, almost intact, but all water is lost.

11. Cokethorpe, known as the Fish House. An estate folly (built on the site of an early corn/fulling mill) housing a waterwheel driven pump.

12. Cleeve, *c.*1900, showing one of the two wheels which have been recently rebuilt as part of a domestic conversion.

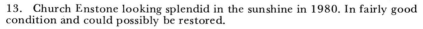

13. Church Enstone looking splendid in the sunshine in 1980. In fairly good condition and could possibly be restored.

14.   The house and mill at Holton *c*.1900.

15.   William Kent added this rustic front to Cuttle Mill to provide a prospect for the local landowner.

16. Iffley Mill, taken not long before fire claimed it in 1908.

17. Islip Mill in the early 1900s. It was quite large, with two waterwheels; only the house on the right remains.

18. The water is lost but some sluice gear remains at Islip.

19. The mill and house at Little Faringdon. The extension on the left with the rounded roof was the miller's office.

20. The small wheel at Little Faringdon which still pumps estate water.

21. Little Clanfield, 1976. The wheel remains and the water supply is good, but there is no other gear.

22.   Taken in 1976 when Lidstone Mill was being dismantled. The gear is stored elsewhere but this large wheel remains on site, together with the large pit wheel.

23.   Mapledurham when working in the late 19th century. The left-hand wheel was replaced by a turbine, now unserviceable, while the right-hand wheel has been restored recently and the mill brought back to work.

24.   (*opposite above*) Swinbrook, the mill on the left and a convenient pub on the right. The wheel is now lost, but the water supply is still good.

25.   (*opposite below*) Somerton was quite large for a country mill. This photograph of unknown date shows the staff, some equipment, and the fine mill waggon. Nothing remains.

26. At Stadhampton the head pond and feeder are lost but this small over shot wheel remains, and most of the gear.

27. This early 19th-century photograph shows the splendid facade of Overy Mill, much as it exists today, with a tantalising glimpse of the fine miller's house (and the miller). Two sets of gear remain in some form and the water supply is good, but both wheels have gone.

28, 29 & 30. The Author's restoration of the belt driven mill from Tracey's Farm and the abandoned heap of ironwork by Lampitts as found in 1975. Now on display at Combe Mill, driven by the beam engine when it is steamed.

31.   Shiplake, much beloved by artists, who protested strongly when the wheel was built in, as seen here in the early 1900s. All traces are lost today.

32.   The interesting small stream wheel at Asthall, date unknown. The site is difficult to recognise now.

33. Upper Heyford c. 1900, the site just recognisable today.

34. The remaining sluice gear at Taynton, of little use now the mill is dismantled.

35. (*above*) An abandoned burr and the last of the trestle support piers on the site of Arncott windmill.

36. A badly-worn footstep bearing brass from Taynton.

37. The mysterious edge runner stone in Christ Church Memorial Gardens.

38. A thrift for stone dressing. The wooden handle is newly made using a draw knife, just as the miller would have done.

39. (*below*) One of the french burr runner stones in Wheatley windmill, showing the maker's name-plate.

40. A fine example of sheet metal bodging at South Weston in 1920. The mill obviously no longer workable.

41. (*opposite above*) Just over the Oxfordshire border, Bledlow Black Mill in 1910. The cloths suggest it might be workable, but the buck is precariously balanced on the six quarter post trestle.

42. (*opposite below*) Epwell, of unknown date and no longer working; however, it can be seen that there were patent sails, a tail fan, and hand chain weathering.

43. (*left*) The cloths are set and the hoppers are full so the miller can relax at Charlton on Otmoor, *c.*1900. Note the windlass in the foreground for winding the mill.

44. (*below*) Arncott, when still workable in 1908. Little remains now but the skeletal frame of the buck still survived in 1945, showing that the front corner frames were extended downwards and ornamented.

45. (*above*) Great Haseley as it finished work in the early 1900s. Still in reasonable condition today because of preservation work carried out by the present private owner. Note the domestic sash windows.

46. (*left*) Great Haseley. Windshaft, cannister box and the remains of the stocks.

47. (*below left*) A glimpse of the brake wheel prior to restoration at Great Haseley. Note the prefabricated shapes which had been fitted under the decayed ring purlin.

48. (*below right*) The six-foot-tall cap finial grounded at Great Haseley.

49. Chinnor, the veteran, working right up until 1938. The brick round-house unfortunately hides the six quarter bar trestle while the uncommon fan is revealed, with the patent sails and striking gear. The mill was dismantled and some parts stored, but now there are thoughts of restoration.

50. (*opposite above*) North Leigh, tidily restored in 1935.

51 & 52. (*opposite below*) North Leigh photographed in 1979—the sad decay continues.

53. Wheatley, of unknown date, and possibly workable. The edge runner ochre grinder has been moved from its working position outside the door on the left-hand facet of the octagon.

54. (*below left*) At Wheatley a pebble is contrived to take the persistent wear of the damsel.

55. (*below right*) Wheatley, a view from the curb during a survey in 1977, with a topsy-turvey finial. Note the short tail beam in the foreground.

56. Six quarter bars at Stokenchurch, the photograph taken possibly as late as 1920.

57. (*right*) The oak cap finial grounded at Wheatley, with one of the tapered trolley wheels.

58 & 59. What remained of Blackthorn East Mill in 1978, and a close-up of the tile hanging.

60.   The windshaft at Blackthorn East had already collapsed in 1900.

61.   The little mill at Bloxham Grove taken in 1910, which regrettably is now beginning to decay. There was a steam driven corn mill in the nearby farm buildings.

62. Little Milton, already in decay in 1900. Note that it did not have one of the locally favoured ogee caps.

63. Great Milton, not so decayed as its neighbour in 1900, but obviously abandoned.

64. In the early 1900s this is what remained of what must have been an impressive mill at Clanfield. The barns remain.

65. Some of the Windrush mills (this is Beard) have this stone slab porch cum loading stage. Beard buildings are now used for farm storage.

66 & 67.   Nettlebed, possibly the only smock mill in the county. It must have been an attractive mill, reduced to the sorry state shown in the lower photograph after destruction by fire in 1912.

Ruins of
Nettlebed Windmill

Chapter Two

MILL MACHINERY AND BUILDINGS

I HAVE SHOWN in the previous chapter that the Saxon settlers were knowledgeable water engineers. It is known, too, that they were able woodworkers and their hand tools are recognisable as being much like present-day ones, but without the benefit of the super metals that we enjoy. Their saws, however, were few in number and ill-suited to convert a tree trunk to workable dimensions. For the lesser dimensioned pieces they would have used coppice-grown timber, and for thin boards they would have used plaited withies. A familiar way to provide the core for walls of buildings was wattle and daub, and one they would have seen used for the long-abandoned corn bins which they must have come across among Roman ruins; by slapping wet hide on to the plaited shapes and allowing it to dry you had a strong and durable container. As for the mill stones, it is known that they brought the sort of stone with them with which they were familiar in Europe.

The parts they would need to fabricate with some care would be the 'gear' arrangement, to transmit power from the horizontal water-wheel shaft through a right angle to turn the upright shaft of the runner stone. Whatever mechanical disadvantages modern engineers will recognise in their mill work it was fairly easy to make, and any worn parts were easy to replace; the parts were fastened together with riven oak treenails, the practice followed through continuing centuries. Any iron parts would have been wrought and not cast, but iron was in short supply and at best was not a seriously considered material.

These simple structures were to be found in this county in fairly large numbers when William the Conqueror's rating authority did its famous assessment.

For centuries the mill would have been owned by the lord of the manor, who was the most likely person to have financed its construction in the first place. His prosperity was assured, for the socage rights he had built in with his mill forced the manorial tenants to have all their grinding done there under direst threat, with worse to befall those found using the old family quern. The servitude under manorial rule finally brought a revolt of the tenants which resulted in a lessening of the lord's despotic power. Perhaps now the mill became a bit of a liability—better to lease it out to a miller and let him have the worries.

9

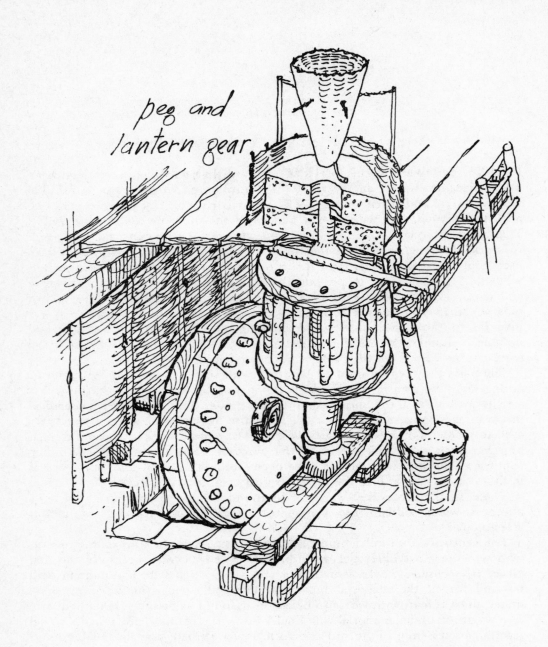

peg and lantern gear

An Early Mill

Despite what appears to be a new-found independence the miller led a curiously ordered life; he was not really in business, for he was not permitted by law to buy or sell or hold stocks of grain, nor was he allowed to charge money for any grinding done. His reward was a portion set by law to be taken from each one's grain which he processed. It can be seen that it would be difficult for the miller not to build up some stocks, and manorial court records show that he was often fined for so doing. There were disgruntled people who complained that those stocks were unfairly gained by extracting a little too much from each customer, a threat to the cottager's small supply which he hoped would last him to next harvest, and court records show that the miller was often caught and fined for that knavish trick, too. The law preventing the miller from bulk storage and dealing was administered haphazardly, closely influenced by a good or bad harvest; it was complicated and troublesome to act upon and it was finally repealed—from then on the description 'Miller and mealman' was boldly displayed over the mill door.

But those very stocks brought problems: vulnerable to attack by vermin and human predators; needing to be kept dry; and needing storage bins for the various sorts of cereals; in fact, bigger mill premises were needed.

At the turn of the 17th century the need was answered by the general emergence of a more substantial style in building. A new awareness of the quality of life showed itself in a desire for something better than the ubiquitous wattle and daub, and masonry and brickwork (long the building materials of the 'gentry') came into use. The miller, now a prosperous tradesman, was able to pay for such improvements as a larger mill building (with the outdated gear replaced), a more efficient waterwheel powering two pairs of stones, extensive work on the waterways, and, best of all, a topmost floor (usually contrived within the roof space) to house those important storage bins.

These are the buildings we can recognise today, all too often in some decay through neglect due to lack of cash in later years, though a few of the mills were prosperous enough to equip themselves with complete new iron gear in the late 19th century, often done hand-in-hand with new premises, or with repairs and extensions to the old. Some have been saved by recent conversion into a dwelling, possibly with the mill work retained; others have survived with their gear fairly complete through the interest of the present owners who occupy what was a separate miller's house. Such a mill is Hardwick, well preserved and featuring a fine carved stone door surround which no doubt had been 'rescued' from the ruins of nearby Eynsham Abbey, while from the same source there are tombstones used to floor the wheel chamber. In some cases repairs were not considered worthwhile and the buildings have disappeared completely; maybe the wheel chamber identifies the site, while sometimes a mill stone has been left behind.

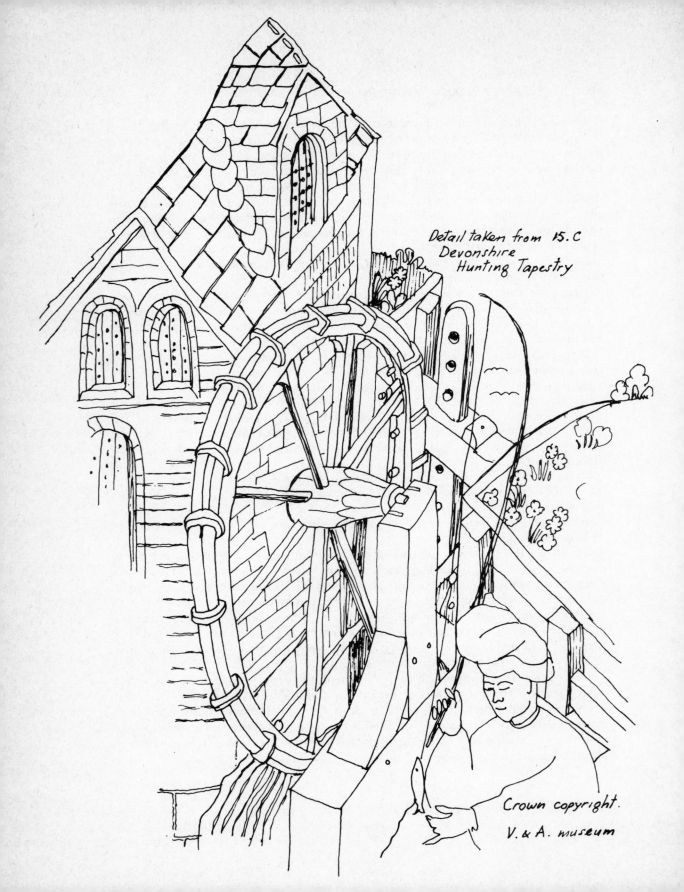

Detail taken from 15.C
Devonshire
Hunting Tapestry

Crown copyright.
V. & A. museum

Traditional roofing materials have created problems. The genuine (mined) Stonesfield slates (actually they are stone) are very durable, but their weight puts an unfair load on roof framing which is past its prime, while the oak pegs supporting the slates fail and encourage leaks. Cotswold slates (quarried) eventually break down layer by layer and encourage leaks also. These leaking roofs have been a focus of decay and the unfortunate owner has had little choice but to replace both cladding and rafters—Barford, you may remember, was open to the sky. The sack hoists, normally built into the roof framing, had to be dismantled and unless there was an actual need they were not reinstated; I have sorted over many a heap of discarded timber to discover what manner of hoist had been in use.

With the change in the building technique of the 17th century came a new layout of the mill work: lantern-type gearing was virtually abandoned and the power became transmitted via fairly accurately made wooden gear trains with two step-ups in ratio to convert the slow turning speed of the waterwheel to 100 r.p.m. or so, the optimum grinding speed of the 4ft.-diameter millstones—a size which was more or less adopted as standard. Iron pintles and bearing surfaces were used to reduce working friction—the advantages of metal had long been understood, and in the history of 14th-century Cuxham there are records of 'Spanish iron' helping out local supplies.

Work we now see done in metal as a matter of course had then to be contrived in timber, but this was more of a challenge than a problem to the expert wheelwright/millwright. Compass arm spokes were favoured for the spur wheels and many still exist, painstakingly made despite being hidden from approving eyes in the ill-lit cog pits, the rims carefully scarf-jointed and ornament added. The mortices for the cogs were accurately spaced and cut through the rim with such care that only the good fit of the tapered shank and a good thump with a mallet would secure them in place till wear called for refurbishing. The butt joints to the rim at Overy (p. 15) worried me till a loose plug, meant to conceal, revealed that handrail jointing bolts had been used; the same joints appear on the brake wheel at Wheatley windmill.

The illustration of the compass arm spur wheel shows how the spokes are halved where they cross. (At Taynton they were in four separate pieces and were 'mitred' where they met.) You can imagine that this particular area in a six-spoked wheel calls for some complicated work; at Overy the spur has eight spokes but only four are morticed right through.

There were exceptions in mill layout. Hardwick, Standlake, and Barford St John all had somewhat complicated gearing.

The usual pit wheel drove three wallowers at 3, 9, and 12 o'clock positions, the two side ones driving lay-shafts and through a second pair of bevels up to the stones, with the top wallower powering the upright shaft to drive the auxiliaries.

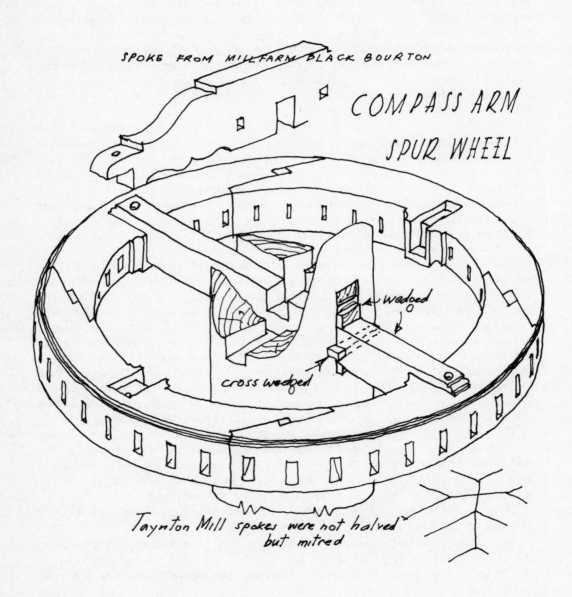

SPOKE FROM MILLFARM BLACK BOURTON

COMPASS ARM

SPUR WHEEL

wedged

cross wedged

Taynton Mill spokes were not halved
but mitred

Overy Mill

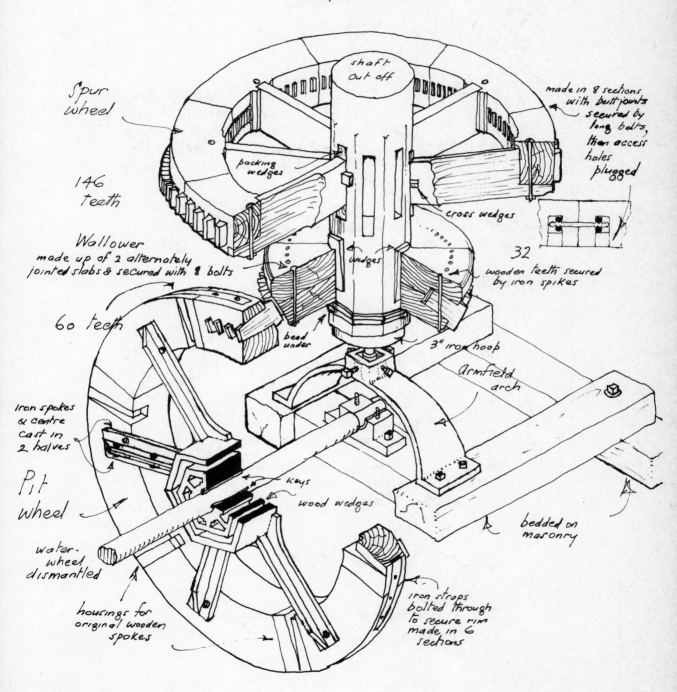

Spur wheel

146 teeth

Wallower
made up of 2 alternately
jointed slabs & secured with 8 bolts

60 teeth

iron spokes
& centre
cast in
2 halves

Pit
wheel

water-
wheel
dismantled

housings for
original wooden
spokes

shaft
cut off

packing
wedges

wedges

made in 8 sections
with butt joints
secured by
long bolts,
then access
holes
plugged

cross wedges

32

wooden teeth secured
by iron spikes

bead
under

3" iron hoop

Armfield
arch

keys

wood wedges

bedded on
masonry

iron straps
bolted through
to secure rim
made in 6
sections

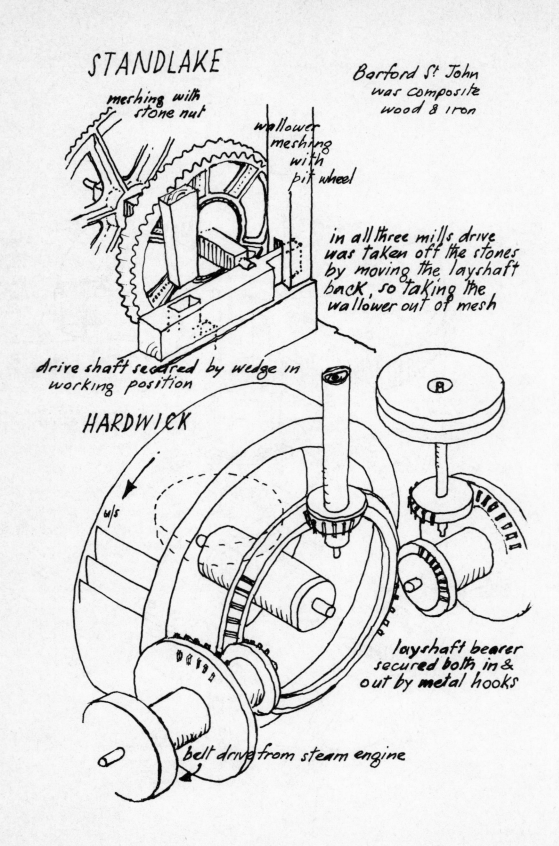

STANDLAKE

meshing with
stone nut

wallower
meshing
with
pit wheel

Barford St John
was Composite
wood & iron

in all three mills drive
was taken off the stones
by moving the layshaft
back, so taking the
wallower out of mesh

drive shaft secured by wedge in
working position

HARDWICK

u/s

layshaft bearer
secured both in &
out by metal hooks

belt drive from steam engine

Adderbury Grounds was rebuilt and re-equipped with metal gear which shows that new thought was being applied in 1870 (probably Lampitt's work). See below where the hoist is unusually driven via a cone clutch. Little Faringdon, so near the county boundary that it might be overlooked, had a refit with stone-grinding gear at a time when roller milling was well established. Here the pit wheel drives an idler shaft carrying a bevel drive up to a cross shaft passing under three sets of stones with bevel drives up, each set supported by cast metal frames of fine design. The 14ft. x 6ft. 6in. b/s wheel must have been powerful, but it is now jammed in the wheel chamber through the movement of masonry. It was the last mill in the county to work; Mr Locke stopped milling in 1960 and sold up in 1970. He died in 1978, 80 years young, after a full life of music-making, clock collecting and repairing, bodging up bicycles, and milling.

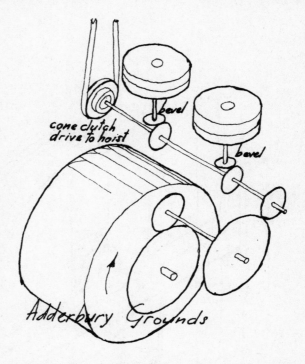

A sack of grain had become established at well over 200lb. weight, and, though the miller was used to humping such weights, his bigger turnover would have reminded him that there was a lot more grain to be shifted around the mill. A windlass and rope haul was a familiar enough sight at the well head, and who better than the miller or his wright to figure out a powered model?

In this county sack hoists were always sited up in the roof where the grain was stored, and a pulley on the windlass was driven by a belt from a pulley on the auxiliary shaft just below. The illustration shows how a hand rope passing down through the mill was used to tighten the drive belt to cause the windlass to turn. On some hoists a chain, running in deeply-recessed pulleys, did the same job as the belt. On each floor a trap door formed by two hinged flaps would be raised as the sack passed up, falling safely back into place when the sack had passed, and by listening for the flip-flaps the user knew which floor had been reached.

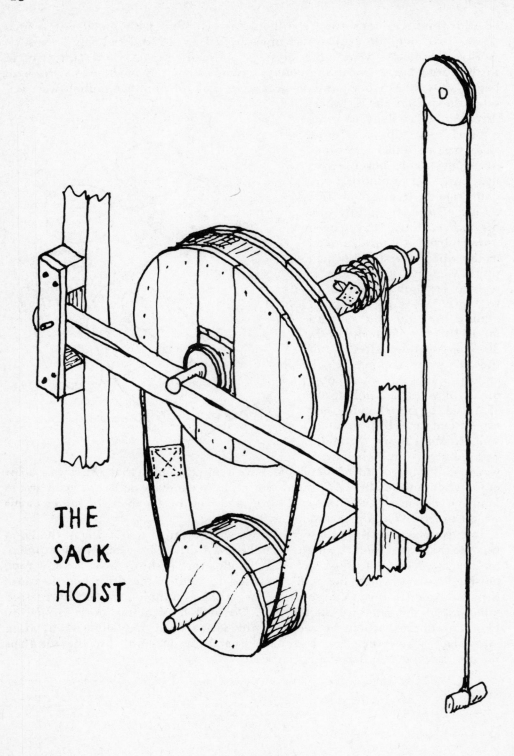

THE
SACK
HOIST

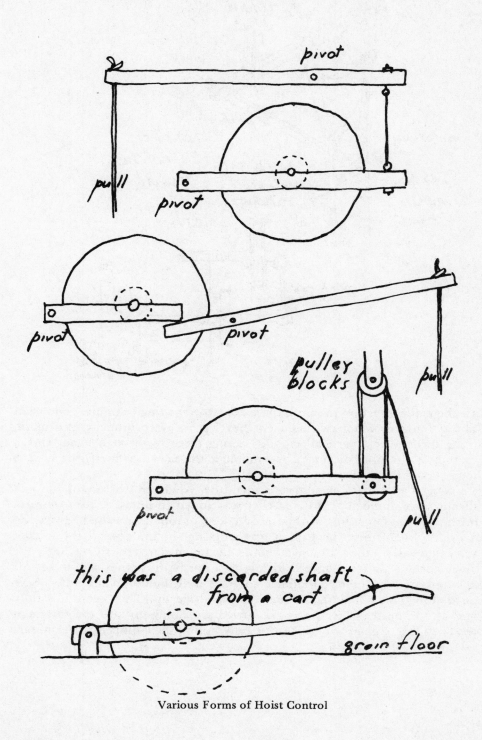

pivot

pull

pivot

pivot

pivot

pulley
blocks

pull

pivot

pull

this was a discarded shaft
from a cart

grain floor

Various Forms of Hoist Control

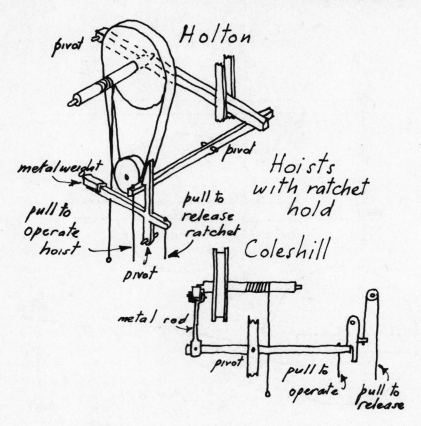

With the smooth action in mind, there are two shocking examples: one went into abrupt motion when two adjacent bevel gears were brought into mesh, while the other was a vertical windlass acting directly through a dog-clutch on the top of the upright shaft; one moment the sack was inert, the next it was being jerked to the heavens.

Dismissing the last two examples, it might be wondered why anyone should complicate such simplicity, but a ratchet was added to hold the hoist control arm in the working position, with a second control rope to release it. It was no doubt useful when only one person was working the mill, but if the ratchet was not released in time the sack could be taken dangerously up into the roof. One or two oldsters have told me, vicariously, how they would set off the sack and race up the steep ladders to greet it at the top, while others have explained how you could sit on the sack and ride up. They were blissfully unaware of the miller's boy who was carried screaming up into the rafters at Clifton; does this explain why this is the only mill in the county with a fail-safe

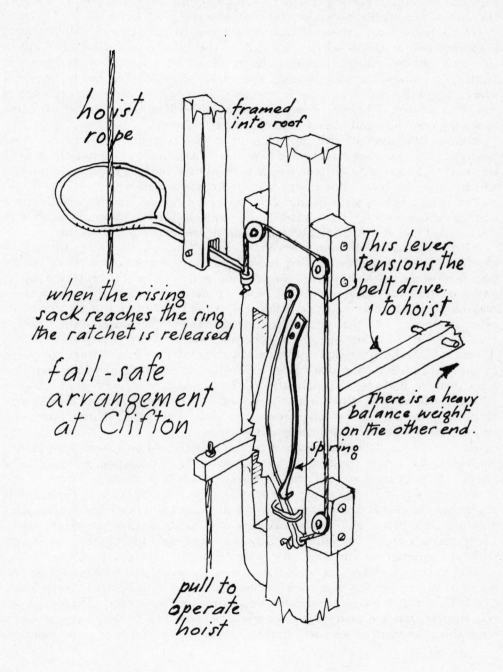

hoist rope

framed into roof

This lever tensions the belt drive to hoist

when the rising sack reaches the ring the ratchet is released

fail-safe arrangement at Clifton

There is a heavy balance weight on the other end.

spring

pull to operate hoist

on the sack hoist? Having reached a critical point, the rising sack knocks off the ratchet—an ingenious product by carpenter and blacksmith.

On the sack floor the grain bins were arranged on either side of a central walkway, and at this level the top trap of the hoist is positioned. At Holton the walkway had wooden guide rails to direct very small wheels on a flat trolley, a convenient way to shift the sacks about in the rather confined space. Right by the trap was a turntable. It seems so obvious, yet experts say it is unique. I believe it to be the brain-child of Ezra Cripps, who had Wheatley windmill, and often worked down at Holton.

Back in the days of the miller's service, the customer received all those parts of his grain which came down the chute (less the disputed miller's portion) and had to do his own sifting of unwanted husks. People were not too finicky; after all, they made stodgy bread with barley and rye.

The village baker, with greater bulk than the householder to handle, used a sifter called a *temse,* with a lad employed to shake it. Indeed, it was about the lazy lad that it was chidingly said: 'He'll never set the temse on fire'.

When the miller became mealman, too, he took over the sifting; he abandoned the slow dust-making temse and devised a rotary sifter driven by belt from some suitable part of the rotating mill gear. It was called a *boulter,* and consisted essentially (in this county at least) of a tube of boulting cloth maintained at an inclined angle inside a dust-tight casing. A spindle turning at modest speed inside the cloth tube carried four parallel beaters. The unsifted meal was fed into the top of the tube and was soundly beaten as it passed down, forcing the finer flour out through the cloth, while the roughage exited at the bottom. Boulting cloth was expensive, so wire mesh, which had first been woven halfway through the 17th century, was used as a cheaper sifting medium. The sifter was redesigned and renamed; it was now a *wire machine.* The beaters became brushes and the wire mesh, in the form of a cylinder, was a fixture inside the wooden casing.

There was the added advantage that the mesh could be woven with graded apertures, the better to separate the minor parts of toppings, middlings, and sharps. A dictionary will tell you that toppings is best bran (as a boy I knew it as pigmeal), that sharps are the middlings between bran and flour, while middlings are middle grade—but of what? If you can believe that there is such a book, *The Bread and Biscuit Makers and Sugar Boilers Assistant* (Wells, 1890) gives a recipe for ships' biscuits as containing middlings or fine sharps, while the superior captain's biscuit contained fines.

Both types of sifters can be found, always decayed, and where none remain we must blame rot and worm for the destruction of their comparatively flimsy parts. The cases were of pine, made with some ornament, and varnished. I will not suggest that we made a poorer job of sifting than others, but our sifters were about as small as you will find—5ft. long, compared with some monsters

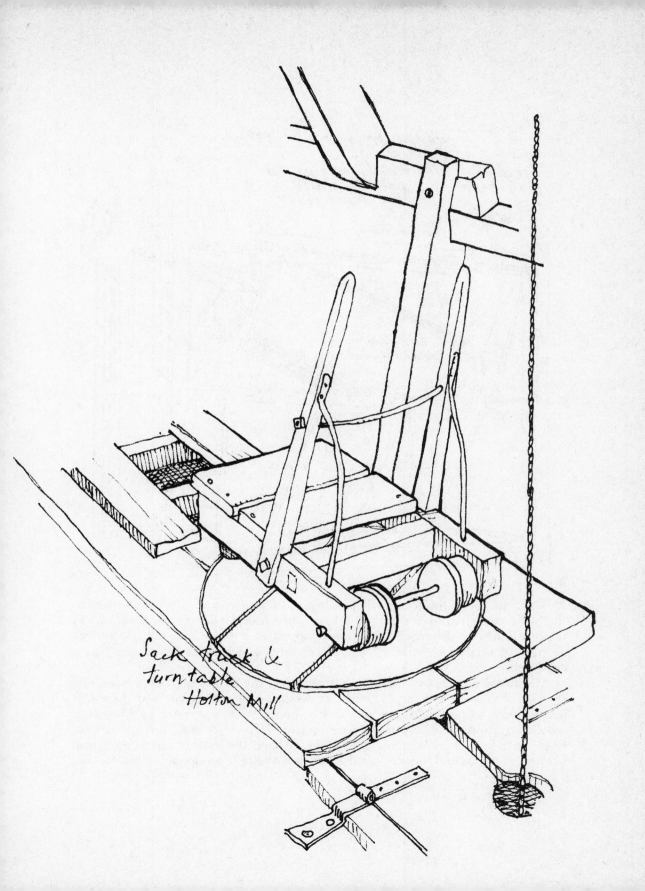

Sack truck &
turntable
Holton Mill

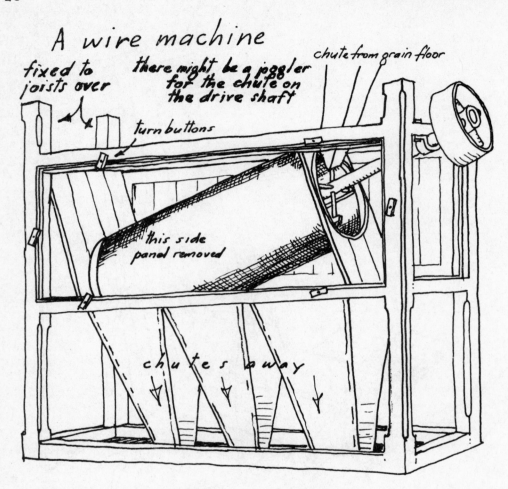

A wire machine

fixed to joists over

there might be a joggler for the chute on the drive shaft

chute from grain floor

turn buttons

this side panel removed

chutes away

of 18ft. or more found elsewhere. A sort of temse, a *jogskry*, was used to rid grain of grit and seeds, but I have only found two still in position. In fairness a lot of the machinery was scrapped as soon as the mills went out of use, especially in some of the bigger ones which must have been better equipped.

A mill did not always work at full capacity; the stones may have been idle through lack of power or of work, or while being re-dressed, and there had to be means to put the stone nuts out of mesh. With wooden nuts a few cogs would be wholly removed from their mortice (*slip cogs*) with perhaps a hook to prevent further movement. A *jack ring* pushed the nuts up out of mesh and held them out; metal 'fingers' on the end of a pivoted wooden lever did so, too.

At Stadhampton the nut, having been raised by means not now apparent, was retained by a pin pushed through the spindle. Salford uses small windlasses and chains. In a few mills there was little choice, with the nuts solid on the spindles.

Another application of the slip cog is found at Dean. The pit wheel has a housing cast in its circumference, and into the housing is bolted a casting of five cogs on a common base; removing the casting and arranging the gap at 12 o'clock would permit the mill to be driven by an auxiliary engine without turning the water-wheel, which was what normally had to happen.

Because so many mills have been scrapped it is not possible to say how many of them were fitted with iron mill work. When any part of the mill work needed replacement it was a time for brave decisions for the cost-conscious

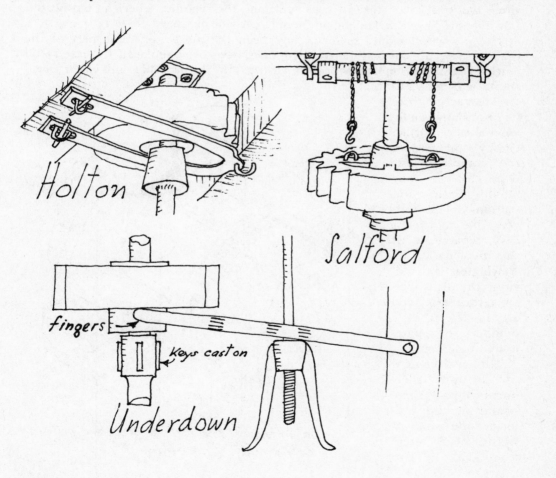

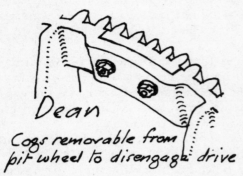

Dean

Cogs removable from pit wheel to disengage drive

miller; not to be overlooked was the time the mill was likely to be out of use. Even when the metal work was prepared beforehand at the foundry, there was still time needed for re-fitting. Phillips of Reading promised a new metal water-wheel at Pangbourne complete in three weeks, but it was actually over a month before the mill got moving again. The Thame millwright's journals show that three workers spent three weeks replacing the wooden wheel at Bayswater, but they did have a steam engine there to provide auxiliary power.

The pit wheel would seem to have been the most vulnerable part of the gear because all the earlier wooden ones have been replaced by cast metal work. The metal replacement was cast to fit the sizeable old water-wheel shaft, and made in two halves to make its positioning somewhat easier. For accuracy of casting the complete gear was cast in one mould with thin sections on the halfway line to permit easy separation of the two parts. At Newington and Lidstone the pit wheels are rather large, and are made up of a number of parts bolted together.

The replacement of the pit wheel might throw some strain on the wallower and soon it would need attention. Cast in two

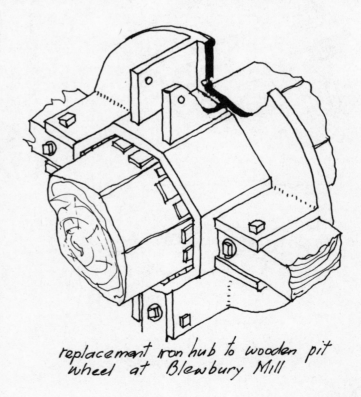

replacement iron hub to wooden pit wheel at Blewbury Mill

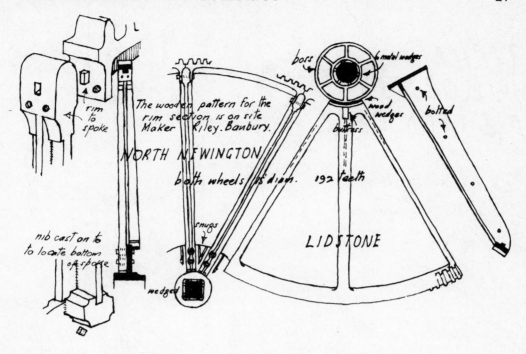

The wooden pattern for the
rim section is on site
Maker Riley. Banbury.
NORTH NEWINGTON
both wheels 5ft diam. 192 teeth

LIDSTONE

rim
to
spoke

nib cast on to
to locate bottom
of spoke

snugs

wedged

boss   6 metal wedges

wood
wedges   bolted

buttress

halves, it would be an easy matter to fit, but because it was not a large casting
it was usually done in one piece and this would necessitate threading it on
the bottom of the upright shaft, lifting the shaft right out of its footstep
bearing to do so. One of the new millers' boys (now over eighty) I have talked
with recalled a long, heavy crowbar being used, but I have yet to find such a
bar lying around. My mill boy looked much too small to be on the end of the
crowbar; he must have been the brave one who went in with the penny which
we are always reminded was put in to take up wear.

The footstep bearing for the main upright shaft was never conveniently
supported until iron came into use, and Armfields, the Hampshire millwrights,
produced a metal arch which spanned the intrusive water-wheel shaft bearing.
Other iron workers may have thought that Armfields held some sort of patent
on the pure arch form and many odd shapes resulted, but they are nowadays
loosely described as an Armfield arch (*see* p. 30).

A few spur-wheels have been replaced in metal, again cast in two halves
and made to fit the retained wooden shaft, while at four mills the upright
shaft has been replaced in metal. It is surprising that so many upright
shafts have survived for they are likely to have been the original ones built into
the mill. Oak, elm, beech, and pine can be identified, and I would guess that
some are sweet chestnut. Many are pierced with the allegedly weakening

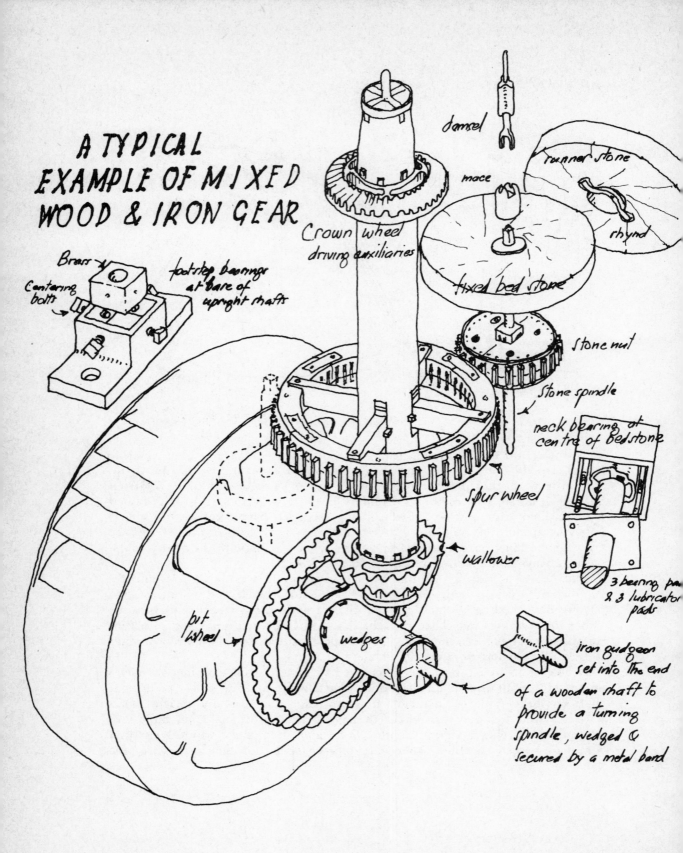

A TYPICAL
EXAMPLE OF MIXED
WOOD & IRON GEAR

damsel

runner stone

mace

rhynd

Crown wheel
driving auxiliaries

Fixed bed stone

Brass

Centering bolts

footstep bearings at base of upright shafts

Stone nut

Stone spindle

neck bearing at centre of bedstone

spur wheel

wallower

3 bearing pads & 3 lubricator pads

pit wheel

wedges

iron gudgeon set into the end of a wooden shaft to provide a turning spindle, wedged & secured by a metal band mortices, merely filled with loose wooden blocks when a wallower or spur has been replaced with metal. At Wooton and Stadhampton, for some curious reason, the shafts have been pierced with an isolated mortice somewhat above stone floor level—perhaps something to do with lifting the stones.

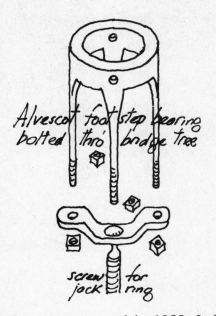

Alvescot foot step bearing bolted thro' bridge tree

screw for jock ring

The hurst framing normally looks undisturbed since the day it was built in, and this is very likely so. Indeed at Overy (15th century) and Barford St John (early 1700s) the uprights have been there long enough to have seen at least three changes in bridge-tree location—did they change the spurs or the nuts, or both? Hursting timbers are always massive, 10in. or 12in. square in section and probably oak. Some of the uprights at Barford excel, being cut from 21in. by 11in. The farmer who last worked Radford recalls that the hursting there was renewed in 1922. It is strengthened with unusual raking stays and has fixed bridge-trees and a specially-made one-off truly vertical tentering lift. The patterns were made privately and the casting done by the Hub Ironworks, Chipping Norton.

Invariably when metal gears have replaced wood the rims are pierced with housings, and wooden cogs (gear teeth) are used. It has been suggested that it was a halfway policy to persuade the wood-minded millers to accept metal replacements, but it is more likely that wood cogs were used to overcome the excessive wear and vibration experienced with metal-to-metal gearing. The extra bracing fitted at some of the footstep bearings does suggest that they may have had problems.

However carefully the wood for the cogs was chosen, breakages would occur and a few adjacent cogs would probably suffer, too, before the wheel could be stopped. The miller kept stand-by replacements, some of which were very rough indeed—anything to keep the mill working—and a prudent miller would watch for wear and even anticipate it by arranging for a complete re-cogging. This service was done by the millwrights, patient craftsmen prepared to spend long hours in their workshops when a hundred or so cogs were needed for a job, identical wooden shapes accurately cut without the benefit of mechanical tools. Fortunately, wooden cogs did not need to mesh as accurately as metal, so there was some latitude in cog profile; but the shanks had to be very accurately cut, of a variety of shapes—tapered all faces,

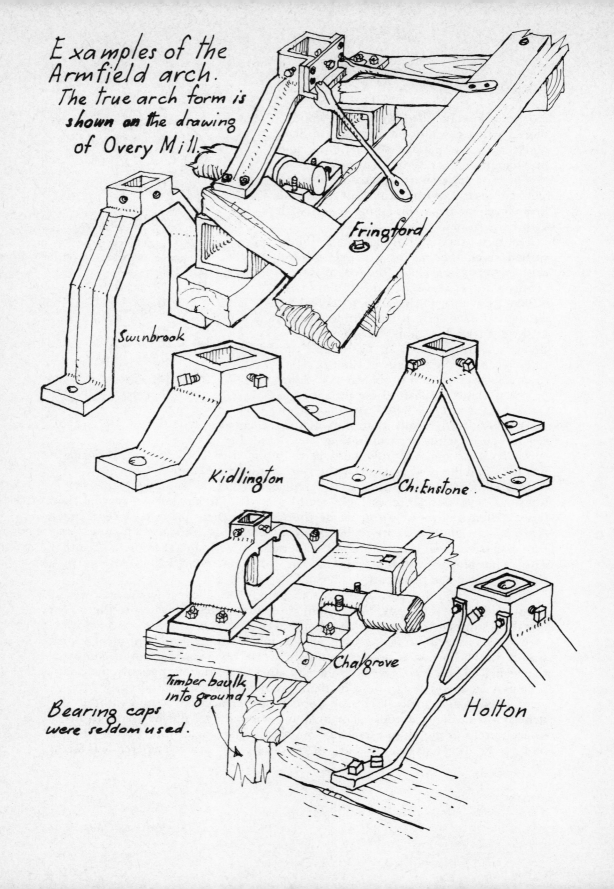

Examples of the
Armfield arch.
The true arch form is
shown on the drawing
of Overy Mill.

Fringford

Swinbrook

Kidlington

Chilenstone.

Chalgrove

Holton

Timber baulk
into ground

Bearing caps
were seldom used.

tapered two faces, some four-shouldered, some with two shoulders. But I have yet to see simpler cogs than those in the spur at Wheatley.

The cogs wedged from the back appeared in later iron-work must have been machine made, though I have had to make replacements by hand.

Some of the day journals of the Thame millwright, Alfred Humphries, still exist and his grand-daughter has been kind enough to let me read them. They show over 300 hours spent preparing cogs for a Buckinghamshire mill. In August of the same year his son went to Brill windmill for a pattern, and then spent 200 hours back at the workshop making copies. In January of the next year 10 hours was spent on preparatory work and 60 hours in fitting the cogs, though the number made is not noted. At the same time they were working on cogs for Chinnor (70 hours), and Bledlow (100 hours), but there is no mention of fitting them. He was the man who built the Bayswater wooden water-wheel mentioned earlier.

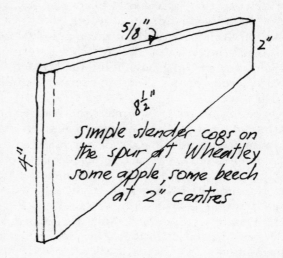

simple slender cogs on the spur at Wheatley some apple, some beech at 2" centres

Apparently the fixing of the cogs was not the end of the job, for the owner of Radford mill recalls being advised, after a complete re-cogging, 'to start 'er up and let 'er clomber a bit', presumably meaning to take off the high spots.

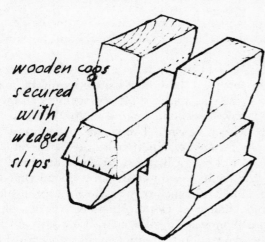

wooden cogs secured with wedged slips

I was re-cogging a bevel gear in public and of those who watched some advised 'of course they always used', while others, somewhat dif-fidently, 'didn't they use?', and still others, 'are you using?'—they were all refer-ring to apple wood. I had to disappoint them; I was using ash, and I also drew their attention to two lots of cogs nearby in oak. It is strange how so many know about apple wood, for other woods were also used, such as whitebeam, pear, holly, box, and ash, besides the reputedly popular hornbeam. I have read of yew being 'incorruptible in use' and Stevens' *Handbook of the farm* (1852) recommends planting hawthorn, for besides providing stock-proof hedges the mature wood can be used for hammer handles, flails, mallets, and the teeth of mill wheels.

On television recently a man who had restored a mill said quite confidently that apple trees used to be grown just for the wood. There are indeed well-established orchards at most of our mills, so that is a possibility; on the other hand I have yet to see a tree big enough to cut into cogs. Standing right in one of those orchards and discussing the possibilities, a countryman who was old enough to have seen it all, said that hedgerow crab apple was used. I had a recent nostalgic phone call from Reg Hitchman enquiring about the present state of Spelsbury Mill. He helped his father refurbish the mill in 1919 and he recalled that they re-cogged with wild cherry. This county, though, used mostly beech. I will settle for that, we have plenty of it.

The time would come when the water-wheel needed major repairs or replacement. If the miller could afford it he would sensibly order a metal one. A water-wheel, not heavily cast, might weigh at least three tons, and handling such a weight would have to be considered, apart from the possibility of having to work in a confined space. A few wheels were cast joined on the halfway line, but generally they were made up of several sections. Earlier wheels will be recognised by the style of construction, with joints somewhat like those used for wood, housing being made in adjacent castings to house a slotted tongue, the parts being secured by cotter wedges driven through slots in the rim and the starts, again secured by cotters, fitted in housing in the rim. For later wheels the more practical nuts and bolts were used to get everything tight.

As the wheel shaft hopefully did not need immediate replacement (there are plenty around to show they did survive), the wheel centre would be made to fit the existing wooden shaft. If there was a later shaft replacement in metal then the smallish diameter shaft (I have measured from 4in. to 10in.) would need provision to fit the largish wheel centre. The same programme of adaption was used for pit wheel replacement. Whether wood or metal, the replacement of a shaft would be a ticklish job, with heavy water and pit wheels to be supported. Yet the late miller's wife at Broadwell said that she and her husband replaced theirs in 1907, told in a very matter of fact fashion. They, too, made light of the actual change at Combe (a new wooden shaft was put in during 1938)—their problem was to find a machine-saw able to shape the tree trunk. Gone are the days of pit sawing on site and finishing with an adze.

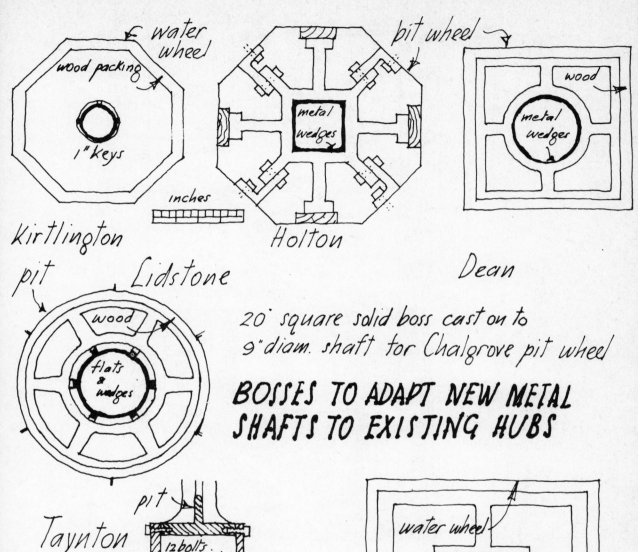

water wheel

wood packing

1" keys

Kirtlington

pit wheel

metal wedges

inches

Holton

wood

metal wedges

Dean

pit

Lidstone

wood

flats & wedges

20" square solid boss cast on to
9" diam. shaft for Chalgrove pit wheel

BOSSES TO ADAPT NEW METAL SHAFTS TO EXISTING HUBS

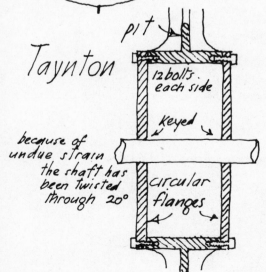

pit

Taynton

12 bolts each side

Keyed

because of undue strain the shaft has been twisted through 20°

circular flanges

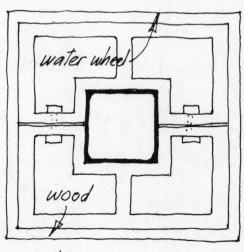

water wheel

wood

Crowmarsh

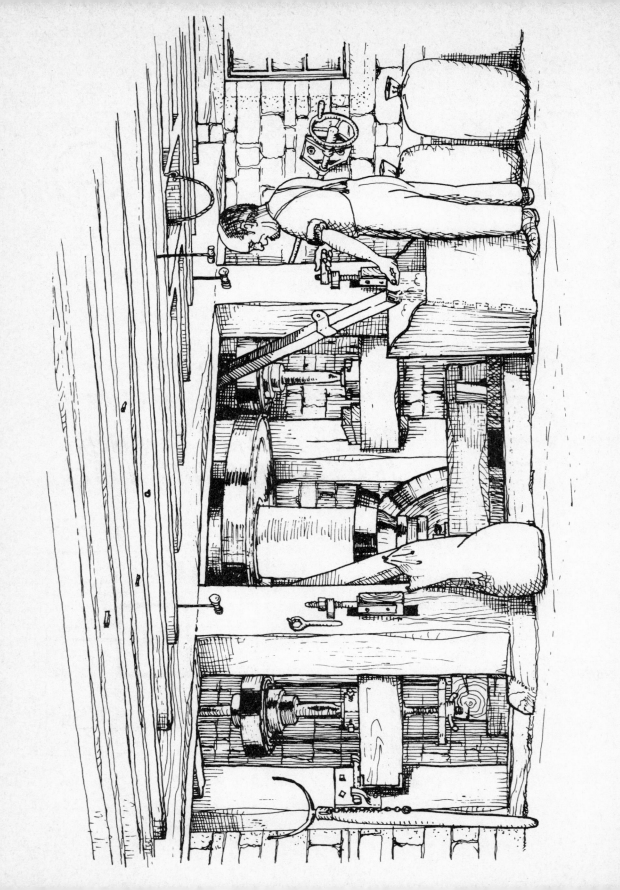

The wooden crown-wheel at the top of the upright shaft would normally have been quite capable of its duties, but with the coming of steam power (and later oil and petrol engines) the miller could provide auxiliary power to his mill at times of low water, and this was done through that crown-wheel. Usually the auxiliary was sited outside the mill and drove by belt up to a pulley high on the mill wall, with a metal shaft taking power into a metal bevel meshing with a newly-provided metal crown-wheel. There was a bonus when water was good; power could be brought out to drive maybe a saw or a chaff cutter. Auxiliary drive was not necessarily brought in at high level; at South

Weston an input shaft drove a second (lower) spur wheel with downward-facing bevel teeth; at Hardwick there was a belt drive to a pulley on the outer end of the left-hand layshaft; at Salford a horizontal shaft carried small bevels meshing directly with bevels on the stone spindles.

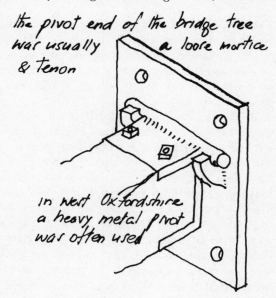

the pivot end of the bridge tree was usually a loose mortice & tenon

in west Oxfordshire a heavy metal pivot was often used

Readers who know their mills will see that I have not described anything particularly unusual in this county; indeed, water-mills throughout England are basically remarkably alike. I believe the one special feature in Oxford-shire to be the heavy metal pivot often used on the inner end of the bridge-tree supporting the stone spindle.

Chapter Three

WATER-WHEELS AND MILL STREAMS

THE SIMPLEST TYPE of water-wheel has flat paddles sticking out radially from its rim, supported by *starts*. When the paddles are immersed to their depth in moving water, then motion is imparted to the wheel, creating useful power. Such a wheel was not a very efficient source of power, but it was likely to have been the prime mover in all our early mills; it was called a *stream* or *undershot* wheel.

A change in level in the bed of a stream will result in the water flowing more briskly at that point, in fact having more energy, and someone must have discovered that a wheel introduced there produced slightly more power. The next move would be to create the situation artificially, perhaps by putting a tree trunk across the stream and building up the banks a little. They may not have had a name for it, but we call that wheel a *low breast shot*; if the water could be arranged to enter the wheel higher still it became *breast shot* and there was yet more power available.

A head of water was often created by means of a dam across the stream (which might even be the wall of the mill), with the banks heightened and a side sluice above the dam to run off excess water into the tail race. On many breast shot wheels there was often a sluice right alongside the wheel to provide a control without interfering with the upper side sluice. A sluice is best described as a shutter (invariably made of stout wood) which forms part of the bank which retains a body of water. Raised or lowered by means of a metal rack and pinion, it would permit more or less water to pass.

As greater efficiency was sought *sole boards* were fitted, spanning between the wheel rims to create a confined area between the paddles, the better to contain the power-giving water, and to contain more water still the rims were made of such depth as to shut in the ends of the paddles. No longer were they called rims, but *shrouds,* and the paddles became *buckets.*

The most efficient type of water-wheel is the overshot, which needs an appreciable fall of water to power it; the water enters over the top of the wheel, filling the buckets as they pass, and it is the weight of the water held in the buckets which does the work as it seeks a lower level (the force of gravity). A waterfall may first have suggested the application of an overshot,

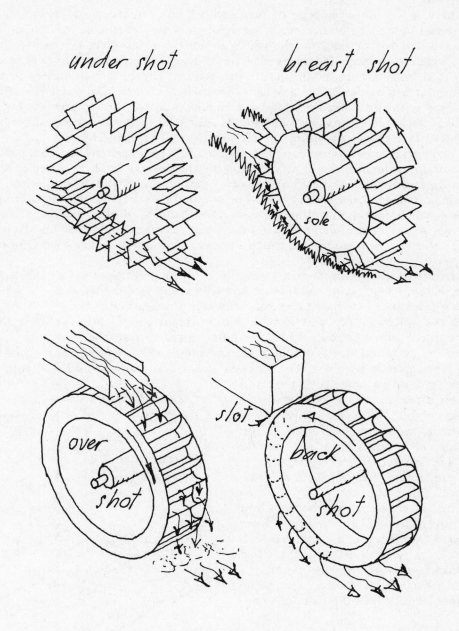

under shot   breast shot

sole

over shot

slot   back shot

but with no natural waterfalls in this gentle county an ambitious miller would have needed to embark upon some expensive pick and shovel work to create one.

There is yet another type of water-wheel, the *pitchback* or *backshot*, an embarrassing choice of names, as we have only two examples in the county. Water is fed to the back of the wheel at somewhat less than the top so, like the overshot, a large fall is needed, and, again, like the overshot, it is the weight of the water that produces the power. The backshot rotates in the same direction as the under shot and breast shot; that is, anti-clockwise when observed with the water entering from the left; the overshot rotates clockwise. With a clock face simile in mind breast shot wheels are sometimes described as 7–8–9–10 o'clock—the point at which the water enters the wheel.

For varying conditions from full stop to full power there had to be some control for adjusting the flow of water to the several types of wheels. With the undershot the whole flow possibly passed under the wheel; when no power was needed the stream would be stopped right off and diverted through a side sluice round into the tail race. The paddles of the undershot wheel had to be set in the water at a level to suit average conditions, and lack of water through drought or too much because of flooding meant a poor power output.

The breast shot, with its raised water level in the head race, had an adjustable *gate, hatch, sluice, shut,* call it what you will, to control the water to the wheel with a side sluice just above it to run off water not required.

If the water supply was from a minor stream and of poor volume, then the control gate upstream would have been used to stop the flow entirely in order to impound the water in a storage pond, releasing the water through the same gate as required. The amount of work available would rely entirely upon the holding capacity of the pond —even a few hours' work was worthwhile when it was the only power available. Sometimes a long feeder would be contrived which would provide storage in the same way as a pond, influenced by the site conditions.

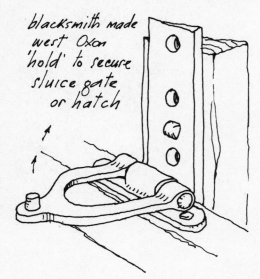

blacksmith made
west Oxon
'hold' to secure
sluice gate
or hatch

The water supply to the backshot and overshot wheels would be from a pond or feeder at a contrived high level, the water making the final approach to the wheels through a *lade, penstock* or *flume,* with some form of control to the flow of water

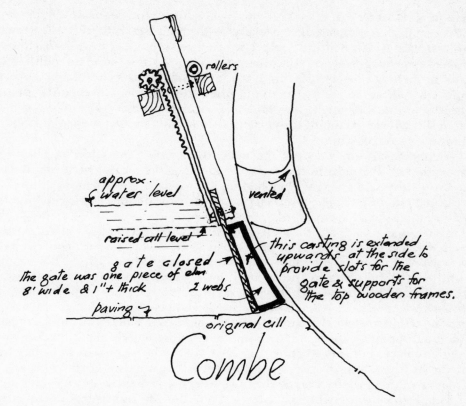

rollers

approx.
water level

vented

raised cill level

gate closed
the gate was one piece of elm
8' wide & 1"+ thick   2 webs

this casting is extended
upwards at the side to
provide slots for the
gate & supports for
the top wooden frames.

paving

original cill

Combe

right at that point. The lade was invariably made up in cast iron (at Radford both hatch and lade are wood) and the hatch control conveniently operable at a point inside the mill building. At Church Enstone a small hatch permitted a flow of water for the sheepwash in the tail race when the wheel was not working.

When work ended for the day it was prudent, in case of a storm, to open the upstream side sluice. A miller worked a 12-hour day or even longer, and in the dark of a winter's evening it would be a perilous, lantern-lit journey for the miller's boy, the most likely person to be sent, and one or two have recalled the fright of it. At Little Faringdon the uncomfortable journey was postponed by providing a bell alarm to warn of a dangerous rise in the water level, though I would not care to eavesdrop on the sleepy miller when the bell did ring.

To all other than undershot wheels it was necessary to keep the tail race clear of water; with too high a level the wheels would become 'backwatered', thrashing away in the tail water and wasting power. An irate miller would have to make an expedition downstream to request, indeed insist, that the impounded water be released. You will gather that water levels needed to be carefully manipulated, especially with mills set rather closely together on a stream which had little fall. The tolerance required between neighbouring millers was overcome by the one who acquired two adjacent mills—Filkins and Broughton Pogges. He used the top mill for the morning's work then worked Filkins in the afternoon, using the water conveniently pounded there for him. It might sound an ideal arrangement till we see the man from Broadwell stumping upstream, fists at the ready to enquire about his morning's lack of water.

George Swinford, who has the delightful country museum at Filkins, can remember all the mills in that area working, and he recalls that when the pond at Broughton was enlarged they had flood problems—an ingenious arrangement of bored-out tree trunks, which he describes as a siphon, carried off the flood water under the adjacent brook.

Storm water and the flooding associated with it has raised many problems over the last 50 years, especially as areas at risk which were once ignored are now labelled 'ripe for development' in our greedy demand for land. Using the control of flood water as the excuse, the Thames Conservancy, which used to be the local water authority, have acted in an arbitrary way and removed many disused water-wheels. When mills are sited on their own streams this has seemed drastic action—surely the main stream should be considered the proper channel for the disposal of flood water. Some of the lost wheels might be dismissed as commonplace, but it is a shame they have gone. The worst loss was the removal of the bottom third of the fine old wheel at Crowmarsh. Fortunately the new Thames Water Authority show they will be more sympathetic.

The wooden water-wheels needed to be well-made and strong; in this county, at least, oak and elm reigned supreme. Always at risk was woodrot, dried out in summer and revived with buckets of water, pounded by floods and miniature ice floes in winter, they even suffered the indignity of being frozen up solid. I heard of this last unfortunate condition being overcome by tossing straw inside the wheel (it was a metal one) and setting fire to it. The firebug was standing in an arched recess between the water and pit wheels and when the wheel was suddenly freed he was trapped in there—apparently millers had nerves of steel besides their other talents.

When the spokes of a wooden water-wheel are morticed into the main shaft it is called *compass arm* construction; however well-fitted the joists are cut they are attractive places for water and consequent rot, apart from the shaft being weakened by the mortices. To avoid chopping into the shaft *clasp arm* construction was used to advantage, though this created equally vulnerable halved joints wherever the spokes crossed.

Nowadays we would not consider anything but purpose-made bearings, whereas simple bearings of wood-to-wood and wood-to-stone were used right

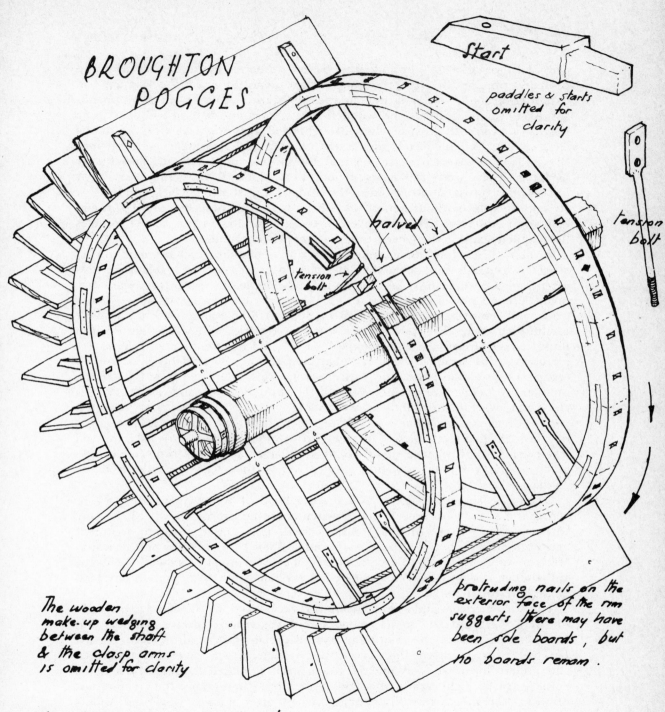

BROUGHTON POGGES

Start

paddles & starts
omitted for
clarity

tension
bolt

halved

tension
bolt

The wooden
make-up wedging
between the shaft
& the clasp arms
is omitted for clarity

protruding nails on the
exterior face of the rim
suggests there may have
been sole boards, but
no boards remain.

This wheel has decayed and has
collapsed into the wheel chamber.

through the early mill period. The Saxons understood the use of iron and probably obtained it from the same surface deposits which the Romans had exploited years before, and they did provide bearings in the form of iron bands shrunk onto the ends of the wooden shafts, turning on hard wood or stone blocks—a type still in use when Broughton Pogges was last working in the early 1900s. A later development was to fit a *pintle, spindle, gudgeon* into the end of a wooden shaft, secured by shrunk-on iron bands and finally wedging. They were called fish-tailed, the spindle having 'fins' cast on it housed into cross slots cut into the end of the shaft. I have found a few straight spindles without benefit of fish tails, and of these Burford Town and Abingdon Abbey shafts have failed—the shaft end has rotted, so the spindles have tipped, causing the wheels to jam in the wheel chamber.

Around 1769 John Smeaton, a man with remarkable achievements in all aspects of engineering, decided to give the different types of water-wheels his attention. An undershot, he announced, was the least efficient; a breast shot might use 50 per cent. of the water's energy, a backshot a possible 70 per cent., and the overshot a winner with a possible 80 per cent. Others who were establishing themselves as engineers by their theories and works rushed into dispute, but Smeaton's careful experiments could not be disproved. True, his credibility was strained when he advocated the newly available cast iron to replace those parts of the mill work most at risk. Millers had great faith in the familiar wooden work and, with little awareness of industrial changes elsewhere, Oxfordshire millers were unmoved. A century after Smeaton plenty of all-wooden gear was still in use in this area, while the economics of the small miller ruled out the site works needed for an improved water-wheel performance. Nor could the larger mills on the Thames do much to improve their situation, spaced out as they were to make best use of the available fall.

Originally Thames millers had created a head of water by building a weir across the river, with a 'gate' in it which could be capstaned out of the way to permit the passage of boats—a *flash lock*. This caused constant argument and even warfare between others who made their living by and on the water. Matters were improved when chambered locks eventually replaced the weirs, and though the mills have disappeared it explains why every present-day lock marks the site of a mill.

The smaller rivers and streams were not recognised for the carriage of goods so there were not the same wrangles, but there were always quarrels and arguments to ensure the continuance of Riparian Rights and Millers' Rights. Farmers who practised flood control on their water meadows, fishermen and millers lived with an uneasy truce, each prepared to defend his rights with a trusty right arm. One law passed by King James they could not dispute: 'the miller stay his courses', when otter hounds were out. Millers

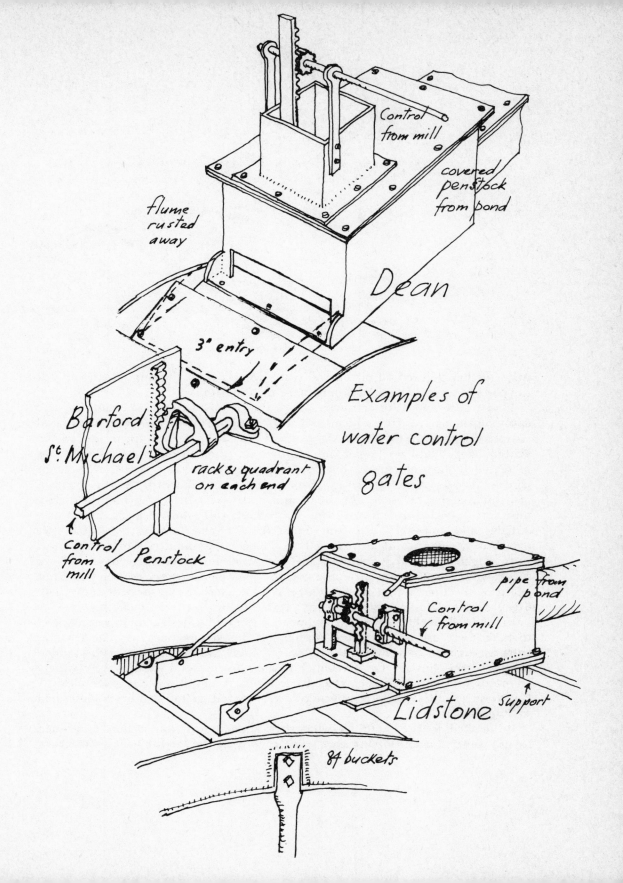

Control
from mill

covered
penstock
from pond

flume
rusted
away

Dean

3" entry

Examples of
water control
gates

Barford
S.ᵗ Michael

rack & quadrant
on each end

Control
from
mill

Penstock

pipe from
pond

Control
from mill

Lidstone

support

84 buckets

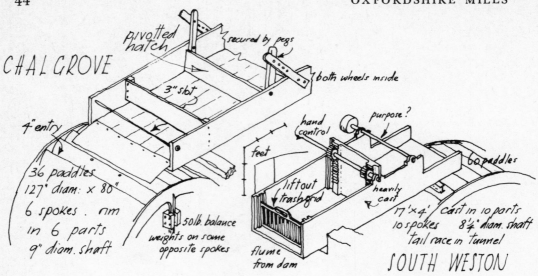

CHALGROVE

pivotted hatch

secured by pegs

both wheels inside

3" slot

4" entry

36 paddles
127" diam: x 80"
6 spokes. rim
in 6 parts
9" diam. shaft

50 lb. balance
weights on some
opposite spokes

hand control

purpose?

feet

liftout trash grid

heavily cast

60 paddles

17' x 4'   cast in 10 parts
10 spokes   8¼" diam. shaft
tail race in tunnel

flume from dam

SOUTH WESTON

were further adjured to check the water-wheel when the hunt was gone, for the paddles were a favoured hiding-place for the otter.

In the 18th and 19th centuries, when that band of emerging engineers were applying themselves to problems, all sorts of abortive theories were postulated to increase the power of the water-wheel. Sir William Fairburn produced the vented bucket and no longer did trapped air expel useful water. Power was increased by introducing a thin controlled sheet of water on to an overshot wheel. It was done at Dean, Broadwell, Cutt, Barford, South Weston, Lidstone, and Chalgrove. At Dean and Lidstone water was fed through a pipe into a closed iron box with a controllable slot (*starter box*), thence into a lade, and smoothly into the buckets. With the familiar 12ft.-diameter overshot wheel turning at, say 10 to 12 times a minute, Chalgrove wheel surprisingly turned at twice this speed and needed to be balanced at this higher speed with weights secured to the ends of some opposite spokes; they had not heard of the theory that an overshot should not have a rim speed of more than 6ft. per second, lest centrifugal force cast the water from the buckets.

In 1824 Poncelet, a French engineer, suggested a design for a water-wheel to make best use of the water. A channel, almost a nozzle, introduced water from below into curved metal paddles. The loyal English millwrights pretended to ignore this upstart Frenchman, but the curved metal paddles were widely adopted, for they held the water to good effect and lifted out more cleanly. I introduced the name as nowadays any curved metal paddle is described as 'Poncelet'.

Influenced in the main by what they already had, our millers continued to use undershot and breast shot wheels. Only in the Glyme valley were they in a position to make improvements, as the steeply-sided valley gave opportunity to dig feeder canals along its sides to carry water to the top of a series of overshot wheels. There were three at 12ft., with an impressive 24ft. at Lidstone.

A review of the remaining wheels shows that seven are entirely of wood; 10 are metal with wooden paddles or buckets; six have metal hubs housing wooden spokes with metal shrouds and wooden paddles; 35 are completely of metal, and of all the wheels 27 have metal shafts. Of the wooden wheels remaining, four are compass armed and three clasp armed, with one of the latter collapsed in the wheel chamber.

Lacking guidance as to local usage, I use the words 'rims and spokes' to describe the main components of a water-wheel. In the Midlands 'rings and arms' are the more usual words—a wheel will be described as having two or three rings and so many arms, according to how it is made up. There is one unusual wheel at Watchfield Mill with only one set of spokes and one rim, the 3ft. wide paddles overhanging both sides; otherwise our water-wheels present no startling designs despite the broad spectrum of basic design. For that matter there was very little produced outside the county to offer example and, despite the brilliant developments which led up to the Industrial Revolution, water-wheel efficiency was little improved. Even Smeaton, after his important early experiments, proceeded to build wheel after wheel of standard design, and only their increased size produced greater power.

In the early 19th century the French government sought better use of their water resources, offering an award for fresh design, and from this the water turbine emerged. Despite its obvious efficiency, England was slow to adopt the turbine (for the smaller miller there would have been a cash problem) and by the time it was coming into recognised use most of the local mills were in decline. The few brought into use are noted in the gazetteer.

On the assumption that some of the metal wheels were cast by the same firm it is surprising that they cannot be recognised as such; only two are identical, an unnamed pair 8ft. in diameter overshot working in tandem in a small pumphouse. Two wheels side by side at Kidlington are identical in detail but of different diameters and mounted on different sized shafts. Only two wheels have internal bracing, one at Traceys Farm, thought to be of northern influence, and the now dismantled wheel at Taynton (probably by Bond of Burford) and set on roller bearings; the 24ft. wheel at Lidstone ought to be braced; those tubular spokes with flattened and bolted ends must have been stronger than they looked.

Three sites, Crowmarsh, Cleeve, and Mapledurham, present a mystery. The outer bearings of the wheels are supported in such a way that they are adjustable for height; maybe I am looking for a deeper reason than was intended, but the arrangement is rather elaborate if there was no serious intention.

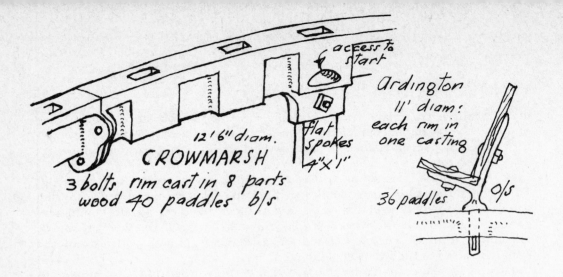

access to start

CROWMARSH
12'6" diam.
3 bolts rim cast in 8 parts
wood 40 paddles b/s
flat spokes 4" x 1"

Ardington
11' diam:
each rim in one casting
36 paddles   o/s

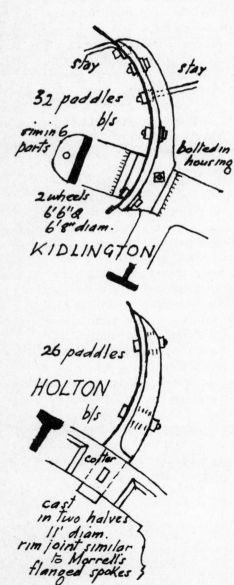

stay   stay

32 paddles b/s

rim in 6 parts

bolted in housing

2 wheels 6'6" & 6'8" diam.

KIDLINGTON

26 paddles

HOLTON b/s

cotter

cast in two halves 11' diam. rim joint similar to Morrell's flanged spokes

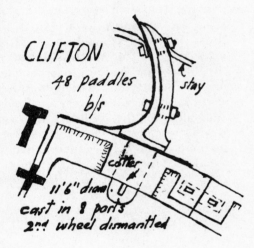

CLIFTON
48 paddles b/s

stay

cotter

11'6" diam.
cast in 8 parts
2nd wheel dismantled

MORRELL'S BREWERY
10' diam.   loose tongue
cast in 2 halves
24 paddles b/s

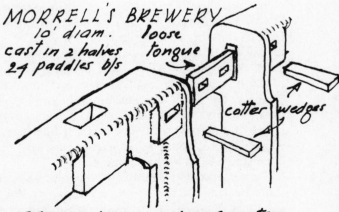

cotter wedges

STANDLAKE cast in 6 parts
9' diam. 24 paddles b/s
FLIGHTS MILL cast in 4 parts
10'6" diam. 32 paddles b/s
tongue & cotter joints on these three

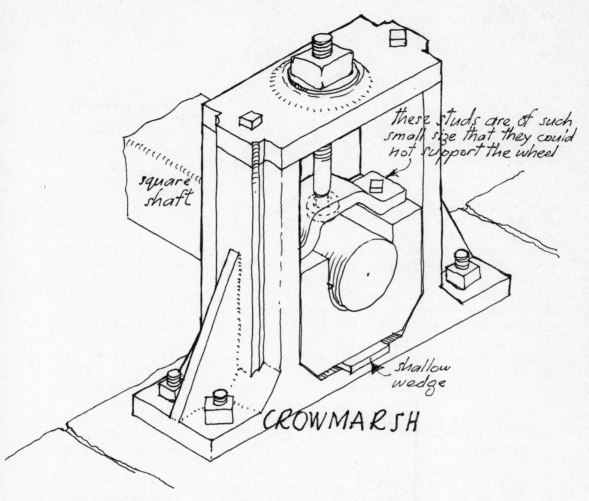

square shaft

these studs are of such small size that they could not support the wheel

shallow wedge

CROWMARSH

I cannot believe that the local ironfounders were not proud of their work, but they did not bother to label it. It seems quite normal elsewhere, whereas there is only one marked wheel in the county, by Lampitts of Banbury, at Salford Mill. There is a wooden pattern of the pit wheel at North Newington bearing the name Riley (it was an ironfounding family), and by a piece of supreme irony I found Rose of Burford cast on a water-wheel in Somerset—they must have done a lot of local work and never labelled it. When checking the area taken over from Berkshire I found a brass plate on the wheel at Coleshill with the name of Phillips of Reading. A metal wheel on a metal shaft has been refurbished by the new owner at Ham Mill, Wantage, cast by Gibbons of Wantage. He has excavated an area to uncover a second metal wheel on a wooden shaft by Guttridge of Wallingford.

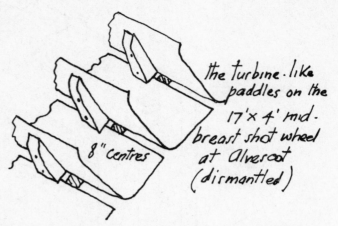

the turbine-like paddles on the 17'x 4' mid-breast shot wheel at Alvescot (dismantled)

8" centres

It might be thought that trade directories could help, but those produced for this county through the 19th century were very superficial, while the men who did the work were just as likely to be listed under 'engineer' or even 'brassfounder'. Such a man was James Lee of Oxford; at Clevely there is a metal plate bearing his name as millwright and engineer, and at St Helens Mill at Abingdon the Oxford engineer, Wheeler, has put his name on a burr stone. Names can be overlooked. I found Lampitts name stamped minutely into a stone spindle, so small that I should have missed it had I not been using a wire brush in a good light—in the dark confines of a dusty mill it would have passed unnoticed.

Both head and tail races of mills were used to wash sheep. People have told how they learnt to swim there as kids; sun-dried waggon wheels sought relief in the shallow tail races, and in some instances they actually served as the village water supply, with a few well-worn stone steps down to water level to mark the spot.

A demolished mill site can be very unrewarding if there are no clues left; perhaps a wheel chamber can be recognised or the water feed (even the tail

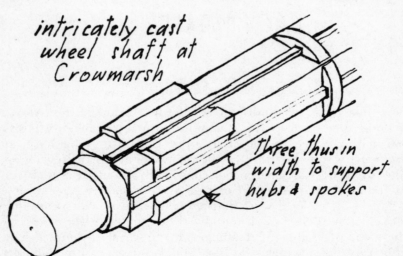

intricately cast wheel shaft at Crowmarsh

Three thus in width to support hubs & spokes

race), or possibly two wheel chambers—Great Tew is a likely site. Islip and Pangbourne are known to have had two wheels, while two wheels can still be found at Crowmarsh, Whitchurch, Overy, Kidlington, and Clifton.

When the recession hit the mills, they contrived to carry on with one set of gear, often with the abandoned gear left on site, and at Overy some fine wooden gear remains. Mapledurham had a wheel at each end of the building (one of which was replaced by a turbine). A 'to let' advertisement of 1791 for that mill suggests that a much larger building once existed, for there was the alternative of six pairs of stones or a tilt hammer and wire-drawing machine— a hidden metal working shop in deepest Oxfordshire.

There must have been multiple wheel drive to satisfy the power demands at Wolvercote, Sandford, and Osney, but I have not been able to discover their earlier layout. Wolvercote may well have had three wheels; when they wanted reliable power they went over to steam. At Sandford they installed first one, then a second turbine (both Hercules), but I found a Gilkes on site, not shown in any records. When Osney was rebuilt in 1845 there was both a turbine and steam power.

Looking back to the 19th century we can recognise the true potential of our meandering rivers; today the production of power is the very last consideration. The natural storage capacity of the ground is no longer employed, as the rain water is conducted to the rivers via such unnatural drainage areas as aircraft runways, road surfaces, and even roofs. Water levels are lowered as wholesale extraction takes place for our insatiable needs, and while, on the one hand, land drainage control for the new type crop farming ensures that levels are kept low, those growers who use irrigation look for a culprit and blame those who own (but do not work) the mills. There are many jealous of their rights, but it is no longer the miller.

Chapter Four

THE MILL STONES

IF WE FOLLOW the events from the water-wheels onwards through the gear trains we come to the heart of the mill—the mill stones. Back in those unpressurised days, when each small community was more or less self-supporting, the few needs they had to seek from elsewhere were the all-important salt, possibly some iron, occasional mill stones, and the essential sewing needs for the women folk. Gordon Tucker, an authority on mill stones, has records of 30 known quarries which would have supplied an immediate local area. Arkell's *Oxfordshire Stone* shows that this county was well supplied with quarries to satisfy a range of useful general purposes, but nothing suitable for grind stones. Cole's Pits, south-east of Faringdon, have been suggested as a source, but the geological map of the area suggests that it was more likely a source of iron, and that the depressions in the ground are probably old bell pits.

Recent excavations of a Saxon mill site in Staffordshire revealed stones recognisable of European origin, so it could be assumed that the most suitable type of stone was known from an early date; that particular stone came from the Cologne district (the vernacular name, 'cullen') and has always been used in the north of England. An equally hard stone has long been imported into the south of England from France ('French burr'), while a less hard (and cheaper) stone which suffices for some of the grinding processes has been brought down from the mill stone grit area of the north ('Derbyshire peaks').

Both peaks and cullens can be extracted from the quarry in one piece, whereas burrs can only be obtained as small pieces; for this reason each burr will be made up of possibly twenty shaped pieces fitted closely together and bonded from the back with plaster, with iron straps round the edge to strengthen the whole. At Broughton Pogges there is a pair made up within completely containing cast-iron frames. It was quite usual to line the feed hole (the eye) with a metal casting, often with a top flange providing a space for the maker's name to be cast into it. Named stones found hereabouts are by Hughes and Sons and R. W. Dell, both of London; T. A. Savery of Birmingham; The Gloucester Millstone Manufactuary; and Corcoran. These are known to have been burr assemblers, whereas Wheeler's name on burrs

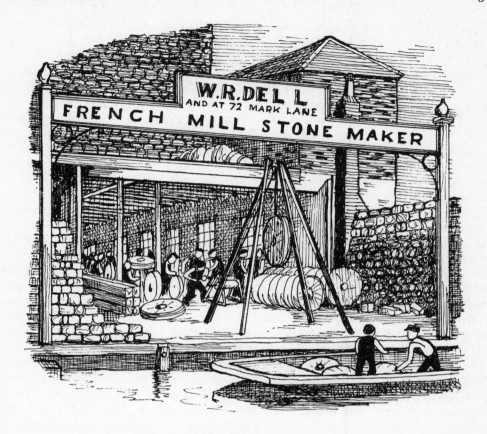

Dell's Wharf, 1850

at Abingdon had probably been added by him to stones made elsewhere, a not unusual practice.

During the long wars between France and England some strange amnesties were negotiated; English paper-making relied for its raw material on a steady supply of rags from the Continent, and there seems to have been an easy-going export/import arrangement. Millers had their needs, too, and in 1809 it was reported in the *Globe* that the export of French burrs would be permitted for three months.

A grindstone arrangement described as 'edge runner' was used for various industrial processes other than corn milling; opposite stones set on edge were trundled round on a circular stone base to provide a crushing action. The only known use in this country is later described at Wheatley windmill, and though they may have been used in other situations the only evidence remaining is an edge-runner stone of unknown origin, preserved in Christ Church Memorial Gardens.

Because of lack of power smallish stones (24in. to 30in. diameter) were probably used in earlier mills, but whatever their size their carriage would have been a problem, being too great a load for a pack horse. In the earlier manorial days collecting new mill stones was one of the services expected from a tenant, with the lord supplying the cart and/or oxen, and such a journey would have been an exciting occasion, since the drove roads and salt ways were ill-suited for the carriage of such heavy loads. In his history of Cuxham, Harvey tells of a journey back from Henley when they preferred to pay to travel through adjacent fields rather than tackle the quagmire of a road.

Those stones would have come down to London by sea and up-river by barge to Henley, which was then the highest point of navigation. The Cuxham men made similar journeys to Wallingford and Abingdon (presumably the stones had been transferred to smaller craft) and one to Steventon which was perhaps a piece of trade with another miller; but their biggest trip was to Southampton, surely for French burrs. Such trips must have been great local events—the excitement of the return with the new stones, everyone pushing in to get a helping hand on them, and the stories of strange places. I am surprised that Cecil Sharpe never unearthed 'Bringing home the stone' when he was collecting our local folk dances.

I have found it impossible to obtain consecutive details of local mill stone prices. In 1567 £15, plus £3-odd for carriage was paid for an unspecified number of stones by Castle Mills; at that time stones cost £2 each at Welsh quarries, but that was not a very convenient trading area for Oxford. *The duty of a steward to his lord* (1727) quotes prices for stones which may eventually have found their way here: 'Cullen stones are sold at the seaside on the north east coast from £8 10s. 0d. a pair 40in. diameter 12in. thick up to £20 a pair 54in diameter 15in. thick; peak stones cost £5 for 51in. up to £11 10s. 0d. for 72in.'. A 54in. by 15in. stone would weigh 1¼ tons, and it is anybody's guess what a 72in. stone would weigh (the thickness is omitted) or how it would be handled.

In 1923 a local miller is quoted (*Old works and past days in rural Bucks*) 'prices have not changed for 200 years'. I have a London catalogue contemporary with that miller which states with some caution 'prices quoted on request'. For some reason a diameter of 48in. for stones was established throughout the country, and though sizes both above and below that can be found, it is the only size I have found in Oxfordshire—there are at least 1,000 stones still to be found in the county, inside mills, leaning outside, and serving as steps and garden features. Burrs fall apart when exposed to the weather and their component pieces can often be recognised when built into a wall; there is a piece built into the churchyard wall at Charlton on Otmoor, a reminder of the old windmill.

A provident miller would sensibly keep a spare stone in hand, but those unused still found in mills suggest that the millers had not quite foreseen that their trade was folding up on them. Still worse was it for the quarryman, who had no direct link with the users and presumably no awareness at all that milling by stones was becoming obsolete; stones in all stages of production can be found in large numbers around the quarry areas, and even the last shot holes made but never fired. (For the curious the map reference for Millstone Edge in Derbyshire is 248 805.)

In the hey-day of grinding by stones there must have been a constant moving around of these lumpy objects—the long haul by ship (possibly as ballast), the trips by barge and cart (or sledge), besides the short-haul buying or swapping between neighbours. Then came the awkward job of getting them into working position in the mill. Various ploys were used: perhaps sections

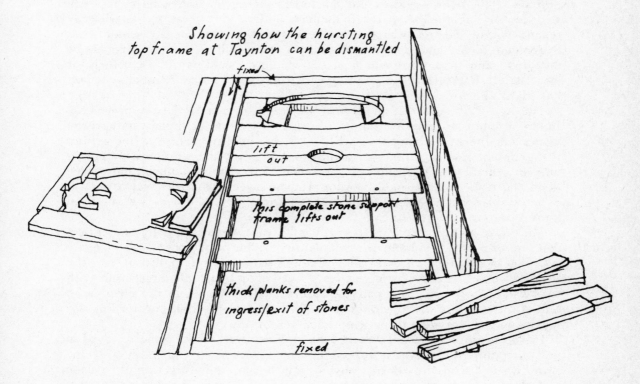

Showing how the hursting top frame at Taynton can be dismantled

fixed

lift out

This complete stone support frame lifts out

thick planks removed for ingress/exit of stones

fixed

Tayton Mill completely demountable hursting

of floor were removable; maybe there was a convenient first-floor loading door; but it is surprising how often it was left to chance. The completely demountable hursting top at Taynton is very thorough. The Thame millwright records nine hours spent in getting a pair of stones installed; he does not show if any ancillary work was done, but he did have the help of a mate. It took four inexperienced handlers to get the stones out of Taynton and trundle them 80 yards up a slope; despite our serious intention we must have presented a Shakespearian comic scene, with a small boy hovering behind and chocking the stones with a lump of wood between heaves.

In 1871, when Robert Stone became tenant of Pangbourne Mill, he 'took to' a quantity of flour sacks, the sort of useful stock that an ingoing tenant would buy, but he also mentions 'took to a new grindstone'. Was this a usual landlord/tenant arrangement? An 18th-century notice offering the tenancy of Spelbury Mill specially mentions that the ingoing tenant must 'take to' the stones already there. Presumably this was a cash transaction beyond the rent to be paid for premises and machinery. It ties in somewhat to an early 18th-century agreement in the Sydenham mills; a document exists whereby tenant Widow Temple was to provide two blackstones in the windmill at Sydenham Fields and one into Sydenham water-mill. 'The stones are to be measured' and then Lord Wonman, the landlord, 'shall pay 20s. per inch for what is left if she leaves' no doubt with the expectation of the next tenant 'taking to' them.

The use of the description 'blackstone' at such an early date is interesting. In an attempt to improve upon the quarried stone artificial composition stones had been experimented with early in the 18th century, but neither their content nor performance is known. A century later composition stones were in general (but not wide) use, and their high carborundum content earned them the name 'blackstones'. Gordon Tucker suggests that the blackstones at Sydenham were not the early experimental ones, but a natural dark stone from known sources in Derbyshire.

The stone provision in our later type mills was two pairs, usually one of burr and one of peaks. If volume of work justified it, but only if there was adequate power available, then an extra pair of stones would be set up, driven from the spur which drove the existing stones. I have described some larger mills with two water-wheels and four pairs of stones, and explained in the chapter on Mill Work how any of the stones could be taken out of mesh, for dressing, for repairs, or because there was a temporary lack of power.

In the chapter on water-wheels I have shown that whilst some revolved in one direction, the overshot turned in the other. When the motion of the water-wheel reaches the stones it obviously influences their direction of rotation and they need dressing appropriately to allow for this. The dressed surfaces are patterned in this county as illustrated. It will be appreciated that such stones rotating face to face will have a scissor-like action (but they must never touch), which will break up the grain which is carried outward and further reduced in the grinding area. The resulting meal is worked outward into the space between the stone edge and the tun containing the stones, and thence down a chute into the bins below.

The illustration showing the miller and his boy working on the stones shows the chute bringing the grain from the sack floor into a feed hopper and thence into a horizontal *shoe*, the grain being shaken along the shoe by the action of the *damsel*. The higher end of the shoe is supported

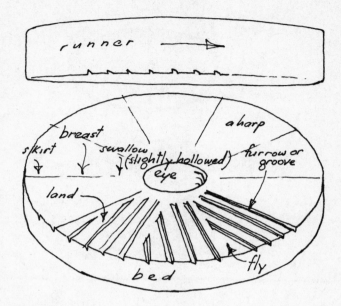

The local way of dressing a peak stone

The lands are dressed with as many as 16 "cracks" to the inch, according to skill. Because of their hardness & texture French burrs are often not "cracked" and even very rudimentary grooves are cut.

on a peg and the lower end by the *crook string*, enabling the miller to decide the rate of feed. Crook strings were later adjusted by prosaic metal thumb screws; earlier it was done by means of a wooden peg (as a violin string is adjusted)—a chance for a bit of whimsey, and, indeed, quite decorative ones can be found. While a floor was being relaid, one was found at Cuttle Mill, long ceased as a mill after William Kent turned it into a rustic cottage. The shoe tended to wear as the lobes of the damsel repeatedly struck it, and hard material (oak or metal) was fixed to combat this. At Coleshill there was lignum vitae, bone at Dean, and a pebble at Wheatley windmill.

Referring to an earlier illustration on page 28 it will be seen that the bedstone lies flat and immoveable (on hursting bearers) with a bearing at its centre supporting the stone spindle; this drives the runner stone by means of a *mace* and *rhynd* which act as a sort of gymbals to permit the runner to be balanced. Illustrated is a whole variety of rhynds and maces found in mills around the county.

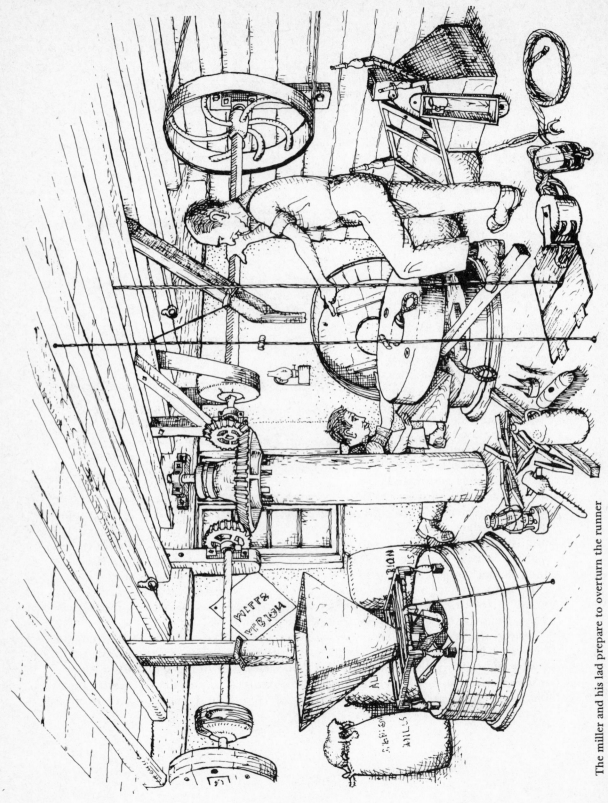

The miller and his lad prepare to overturn the runner

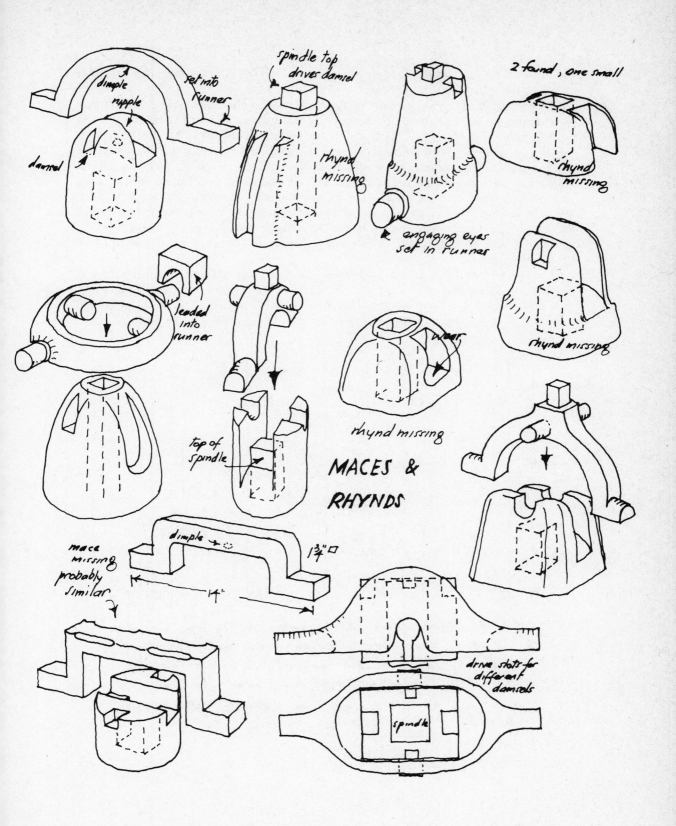

dimple
nipple
set into runner
damsel

spindle top drives damsel
rhynd missing

2 found, one small

rhynd missing

engaging eyes set in runners

leaded into runner

top of spindle

rhynd missing

wear

rhynd missing

MACES &
RHYNDS

mace missing probably similar

dimple →

14"

1¾"□

drive slots for different damsels

spindle

The action of *tentering* is part of the expertise of the miller, the gap between the stones being a critical adjustment for the proper processing of the cereals and legumes likely to be put through the mill. The adjustment is affected by raising or lowering the bridge-tree which supports the stone spindle which in turn supports the runner. This adjustment was made in earlier days by simple wedges, and indeed this method can still be found in use, but as metal came into use screw jacks of many forms were contrived with greater assurance of staying put. This county is the only one where the rear mortice and tenon at which the bridge-tree pivots is replaced by a heavy type of hinge (p. 35), though I did find just one that had escaped to Lacey Green windmill in Buckinghamshire.

For proper milling it was necessary to keep the stones in good grinding condition. Normally the amount of work done would decide the occasion for re-dressing, but woe betide him who failed to notice that the hopper had emptied, for without grain between them grinding areas could come to harm

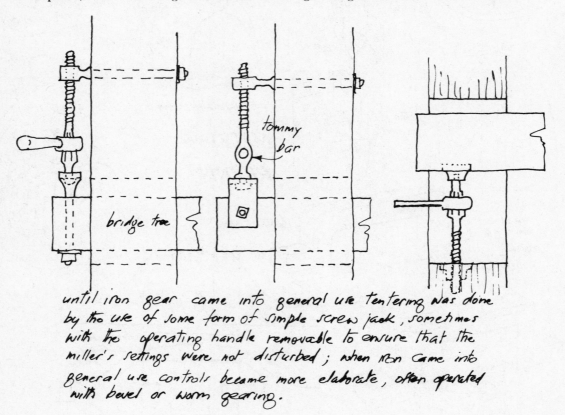

until iron gear came into general use tentering was done by the use of some form of simple screw jack, sometimes with the operating handle removable to ensure that the miller's settings were not disturbed; when iron came into general use controls became more elaborate, often operated with bevel or worm gearing.

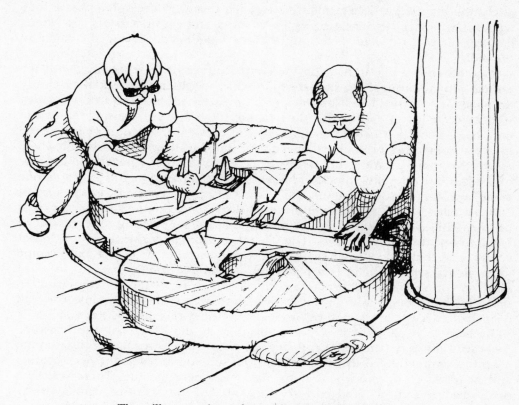

The miller tests the surface while his son does the work

and emergency work be called for. Bell alarms were used to warn of this, and though I have found the small brass bells lying around I have never found one rigged in position. This was probably because we used the simplest form, with the bell strap buried in the grain in the hopper. When the level got low the strap would be uncovered and let the bell hang free to ring in sympathy with the general vibration. One who had better remain unnamed used to pinch off to the inn and as like as not have to break into a gallop on his way back when his trained ear told him all was not well—why do I never get worthwhile information from these old boys?!

It was an advantage for the miller to be able to do his own stone dressing, especially if the mill was otherwise idle, or just one pair of stones was working. If he had neither the skill nor the time there were travelling men who would present themselves for work. They had a reputation for needing much liquid refreshment which caused a certain unpredictability, but maybe the dusty, gritty job justified it. When milling was going through developing phases they would have been the messengers of changes and improvements elsewhere, chatting after light had failed and before bedding down for the night in the mill.

Page 56 shows the activity on the stone floor prior to redressing, with the critical job of turning the runner stone which might well break if carelessly dropped. In our small mills, stones were 'overturned' by means of a wooden wedge and a lot of faith, with no relaxing till the stone was safely pillowed on a bag of chaff. It could be that rope and tackle were used, for heavy metal eyes can sometimes be found screwed into the main wood bearers somewhere above the stone position, but as evidence I can say that I have found plenty of wedges but no pulley blocks. I know a metal gallows-type lifting gear (stone crane) was used at Bletchington and Cassington, and surprisingly at the ancient Arncott windmill. Continual use meant the gradual reduction in the thickness of the stones; eventually the rhynd would need re-setting and the metal bands round the burrs moved. The Thame millwright writes so often 're-set centre bar' that I wonder if sometimes it was because the rhynd had become loose in its setting—in fact, a repair job. When the runner became so worn as to be at real risk of breaking when handled, it would be transferred to the safer bed-stone position, and a new runner, stored over against the wall over the last few years, would be brought into use with some satisfaction.

Because it is so seldom seen the bearing in the centre of the bedstone presents a mystery, though there will be sight of the lower part of it from the cogpit. Examination of discarded stones will sometimes reveal the neck bearing still in position, or enough of it to make it understandable. There will be a metal casting securely wedged into the centre of the bedstone, made with at least three housings to locate bearing pads; these may be brass (if they have not been stolen), but if you find brown powder that will be the decayed remains of hardwood pads. Where there are six housings, three will be for bearing pads and three for grease or tallow impregnated softwood or tow; maybe not a very acceptable method of lubrication to cope with 100–120 r.p.m., but one well established by custom. A concerned miller might cram the fattier parts of mutton or bacon into the spaces. Adjustment of a worn neck bearing may have meant dismantling and putting packing behind the pads. A more practical way was to have long bolts, adjustable from the cogpit, the heads of the bolts being long square tapers abutting on the tapered backs of the bearing pads.

Halfway through the 19th century roller milling, as opposed to stone grinding, came into use in Europe. A much finer flour was produced which England was quick to import; I imagine that the delicate cakes and pastries which could be made from it appealed to Victorian gentility. The first rollers to come out of Europe were made of the rather unlikely material, porcelain. Later, improved metal techniques produced chilled iron rollers. Milling by rollers seems to have been anticipated, for a patent taken out in Birmingham as early as 1776 described how the cast-iron rollers be annealed, ribbed, and then hardened by heating in hoof and horn parings; the inventor, crying in the wilderness, claimed he could grind 'malt, barley, wheat, beans, etc., normally ground in what are called steel mills'. This reference to steel mills suggests that there was already an awareness of grinding other than by stones.

The larger mills able to afford the new roller milling processes (it was linked with more sophisticated cleaners and sifters) did so to fight off the overseas threat. Few in this county could consider such ambitious changes, and the few who did failed to survive. Commenting on the times (*Modern flour milling,* 1897) Voller stated 'roller milling can no longer be looked on as an experiment; in country districts a few stone grinding mills will doubtless produce a little flour . . .'. He goes on to describe small millers as having a throughput of 300 sacks per week. Well, this was a country district of small millers, in fact, with a lesser throughput than 300 sacks, but even if those small millers

An abandoned Derbyshire mill stone quarry

had read Voller they would have been little influenced by him, well aware that they had to manage with the power available to them and the mill machinery they had inherited.

Once through the stones, once through the sifter, and as for washing the grain and taking out foreign bodies, that would have caused hearty bucolic laughter and the quotation—'you've got to eat a peck of dirt before you die'.

Chapter Five

APPLIED POWER

WHILE PRE-HISTORIANS squabble about who first used water power and for what purpose, we can look at a more recent period, when the Saxons in Oxfordshire set up their water-driven corn mills and fulling mills.

When cloth has been woven its quality is improved by working filling agents into the weave (notably fuller's earth), and when small batches have to be treated this can be done by trampling the fabric in vats. It is a measure of man's ingenuity that he found a way to harness the water-wheel to do this job. To do so he evolved yet another principle—the cam. One application of it was to provide radial pegs in the wheel shaft. These engaged with other pegs set in vertical timber baulks which were successively dropped on to the cloth as the shaft rotated; I have heard this described as a beetling machine. The second application is for the pegs to be set into a wheel rim parallel to the shaft, and they actuate wooden hammers which 'beat' the fabric. Both types were used for fulling and also for washing and scouring the raw fleeces. In later years they came into use in the paper-making trade.

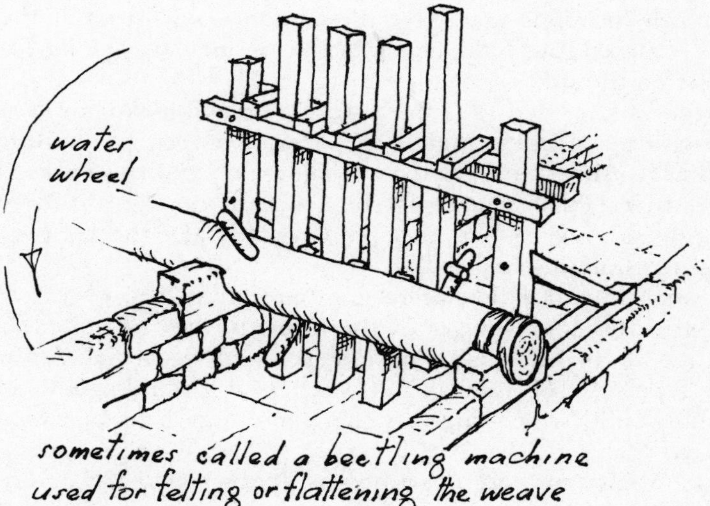

Before the cloth trade became established in recognised areas there must have been fulling mills operating willy nilly as the need arose, maybe as a piece of speculation by a landowner, or built and operated by a religious house. Their

water wheel

sometimes called a beetling machine
used for felting or flattening the weave

63

former existence is
sometimes recorded
on maps by the
Tucking Mill
streams; tucking is
another name for
the fulling process.
At the Dissolution
of the Monasteries
some effort was
made to retain the
monastic fulling
mills and keep them
in work, offering
help for the needy,
and training for
would-be artisans
(The Statute of

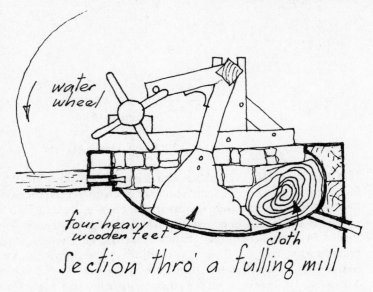

Section thro' a fulling mill

Artificers). In 1546 the sum of 18 shillings was spent 'for one myllstock
for the fulling mill at Osney' besides an unspecified sum for blacksmith's
work, presumably to put the mill back into working condition. Mr Stumppe,
a clothier already operating a similar mill at Malmesbury Abbey, sought a lease.
Requirements of the tenant were that 'he must find work for 2,000 people
from time to time in clothmaking, for the succour of the city and county
about, for which purpose the mills were made'. Two thousand does seem a
daunting number, and Mr Stumppe may have thought so, too, for while there
is no record that he worked the mill, he did make money by selling lead,
glass, wood, and iron from the site.

In 1555 a committee was formed in Oxford 'to devise and make bonds and
indentures and otherwise for a fulling mill to be set up between Hythe Bridge
and Rewley Wall'. Rewley Abbey had not had a fulling mill and this looks like
a philanthropic effort to establish a completely new mill on the abandoned
abbey site. Mr Mallyson, a City draper, was prepared to take the lease, but
there is no record that the mill was ever built.

In 1572 the city weavers and fullers were granted a franchise over a five
miles radius round Oxford; the advantages of the franchise are not stated, but
one condition was that 'every fuller must have eleven courses of handles and
two pairs of shears at least'. At this time an Act was passed forbidding a weaver
from operating a fulling mill, which suggests that there may have been some
dissent between the two trades.

The fulling mills at Abingdon were described as decayed in 1538 and had
been rebuilt by 1557; two of them were worked on the same water as the

Abbey Corn Mill and had to give preference when water was low. There are records relating to the Grove Corn Mill showing a fulling mill 'lately set up' in one of them in 1751, but it was back to corn only in 1812. Successive leases relating to Grove mention two corn mills, while a lease of 1829 specifically states 'formerly two corn mills', but there were two working in the early 1900s, so it looks as if milling had its ups and downs.

One of the Clevely mills was fulling in 1643, but later documents dither between corn and fulling, so maybe both tasks were done; the lower mill at Clevely was rebuilt and equipped for corn by Lampitts in the later 19th century. One of the Burford corn mills (vague documents cause much confusion) was operating as two fulling mills up to 1848, and was then converted back to 'two corn mills and one seed mill'; the Town Mill may well have had two water-wheels before it was rebuilt as a pump house.

In the north of the county Fulling Mill Farm, to the west of Broughton, marks the site of an abandoned fulling mill; Richard Davis's map shows this as 'Upper Fulling Mill', so can we assume that there was yet another downstream? If so, one of them had been converted to paper-making and was worked by Lewis Stone, who was made bankrupt in 1807. Francis Tilbury (with paper interests elsewhere) took the place over. There is some confusion because Lewis Stone is also shown working North Newington, whereas the Cobb family were in that mill till at least 1816.

I continue with the tale of paper later. Meanwhile the cloth industries of Oxfordshire eventually became established in specific areas; on the Windrush above and below Witney and to the west of Chipping Norton and Banbury.

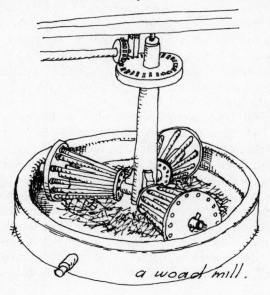

a woad mill.

The Rev. Giles, who wrote of Witney and Bampton in the 1850s, makes great mention of the tucking mills and quite overlooks their corn-milling activities. Dyeing and the production of dyes must have gone on wherever the cloth trade was established. Woad was prepared in the Banbury region (there is still a Woad Mill Farm) and the plant was grown as a cash crop in the area. In preparation the leaves were crushed, made into balls and dried, crushed again and left to ferment. This part of the process made such a stench that Elizabeth I insisted that the mills cease operation when she was passing. I have a print of a 16th-century woad mill with horse-driven wooden rollers akin to edge runner stones, and needing no great contrivance to drive by water power.

The history of the Witney blanket trade is ill-recorded. The actual weaving was done by hand until steam power took over; certainly it was never done by water power, but scouring and fulling had been by water power from an early date, and other processes were gradually incorporated. Apart from the corn/fulling mills in the area there were two individual fulling mills recorded in 1223 and three in 1277.

In the second half of the 17th century Dr Plott wrote that Witney had 60 weavers operating (owning ?) 150 looms with some three thousand poorly-paid people of all ages engaged in teasing out and spinning the yarn. Unlike the Rev. Giles, he overlooked the fullers; very strange, for there must have been quite a number engaged in their kindred tasks. Queen Anne had granted the Witney woolworkers in 1708 an advantageous charter covering a 12-mile radius round the town, and one wonders if it still had any authority in the later 1700s. At that time the industry began to take on a new pattern, with the woolmasters owning more and more of the looms and employing people to operate them. The woolmasters pooled resources to install and share the first gig mill (for raising the nap) in 1782, whereby one man and two boys could do the work of 18 men and six boys, but there is no record that it was water-powered.

By 1790 the first spinning frame powered by water was being installed, offering a considerable threat to the raggle-taggle army of spinners. Yet there does not seem to have developed the industrial unrest noted in Lancashire and Yorkshire; possibly the trade was so long established in Witney under the benevolence of a few families that respect was automatic, though it is difficult to overlook the mysterious death of an early advocate of power spinning who was found drowned in the wheel chamber at New Mills.

The machinery of the wool trade underwent considerable development in the north of England during the Industrial Revolution, and the Witney woolmasters sensibly noted the changes taking place, prudently buying new equipment when all the snags had been overcome. To house the developing plant the erstwhile corn-mill premises needed to be constantly enlarged and they finally blossomed into large new factory-style buildings, though by tradition spinning and fulling remained separate. As soon as the steam engine was seen to be reliable it was adopted in place of water power. The Windrush had served well the small corn mills, but was not up to industrial demands. Worsham Mill made best use of the power available by installing a turbine. New Mills, basically a spinning mill, managed to the last with two 15ft.-diameter wheels on the same shaft, the water feed controlled unusually by a 'roller blind' made of leather.

The gig machines (rowing machines), whose task it was to raise the nap of the fabric, used wooden rotating rollers furnished with hundreds of teasel heads. The teasels were grown locally as a cash crop to provide for the insatiable demand. I have talked with people who have tentative memories of the teasel crops—do we recall what we actually saw or what we were told about?—though the sight of a field of teasels standing seven feet tall and 12,000 to the acre would not be forgotten. Most older people remember the ranges of tentering racks, and some say they remember drying sheds for the teasels.

Writing of Oxfordshire farming in 1854, C. S. Read mentions the growing of flax in the mid-west of the county. Earlier, in 1838, a flax mill was installed in one of the Ducklington mills. Flax was threshed by flail, steeped in water and then scutched, and it was this latter process which was described as very tedious and expensive, which no doubt explains the installation of flax mills (scutchers) where there was some spare water power to be used. The scutchers took the same form as the beetling machines described earlier in this chapter; such apparatus was installed in the early 1850s in Combe Mill, which had ceased as a corn mill at that time and had become the Blenheim Estate complex for wood sawing and estate repairs, still using water power.

On that agricultural note we can move naturally to another basic activity. As a better understanding of land husbandry spread from the eastern counties, there came a need to broadcast bone meal on the land, something beyond the customary animal manure and lime. Water power was inevitably used for the bone grinders, and though water-mills may have been taken over and adapted (or even shared), some bone mills were built specially, notably Old Chalford and Great Tew. Looking for extra trade, a grinder was installed at Crowmarsh. In 1845 Osney had been rebuilt, equipped with four pairs of burrs, wood saws, and a bone mill. North Newington, long a prosperous paper mill, appeared in the directories of 1871 under 'artificial fertiliser' and in the *Banbury Advertiser* there appear irate letters about the far from artificial smell. Some of the grinding mill buildings remain, but none of the plant, and one wonders about its size and output. At Standlake Mill there are the remains of one small machine labelled Bentall's Bone Mill which ground by means of ribbed metal rollers; I was told it was used to provide poultry grit.

As farm crops yields increased, threshing by flail became uneconomic and barn threshers driven by wind and water power came into use on English farms, although Oxfordshire changed a little later and used the more impressive outfits powered by steam traction engines. However, there was one farm where a water-wheel powered a whole range of farm machinery on the Great Tew Estate. I know the Boulton family once owned the estate and I like to think that James Watt (the families were in business) may have had a hand in the

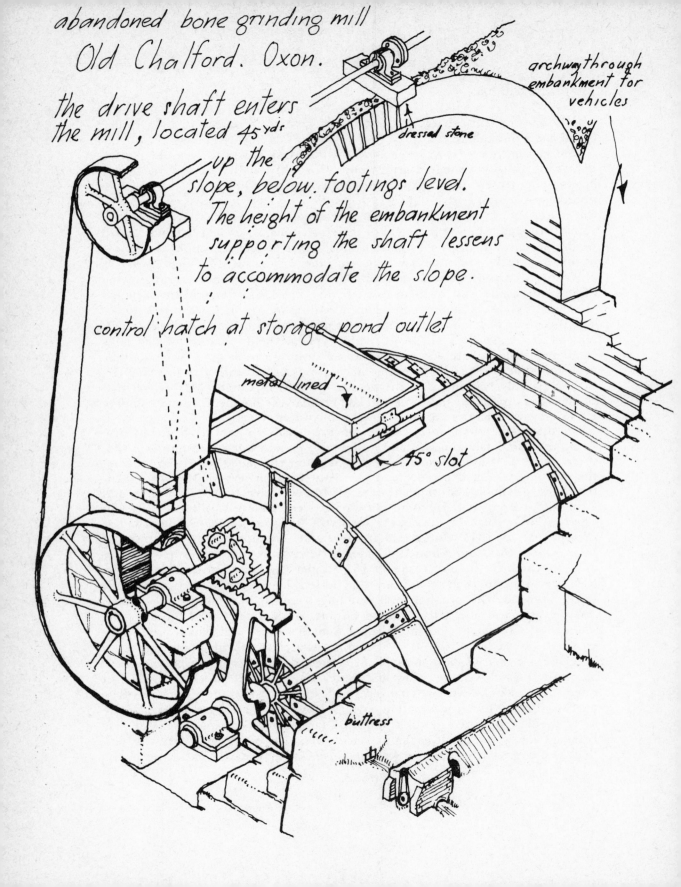

abandoned bone grinding mill
Old Chalford. Oxon.

the drive shaft enters
the mill, located 45 yds
up the
slope, below footings level.
The height of the embankment
supporting the shaft lessens
to accommodate the slope.

archway through
embankment for
vehicles

dressed stone

control hatch at storage pond outlet

metal lined

45° slot

buttress

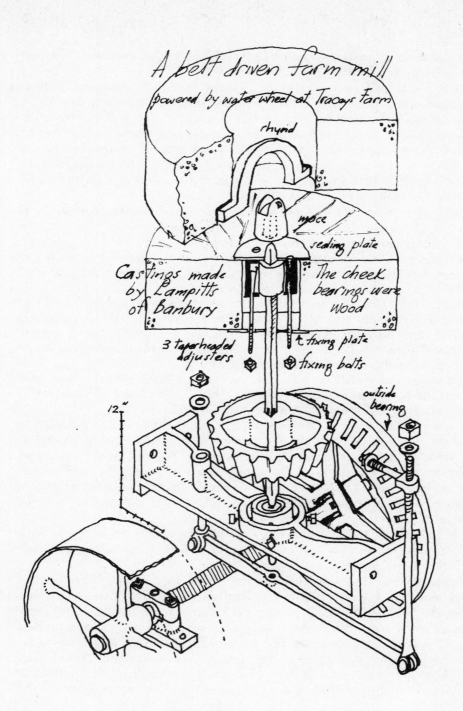

A belt driven farm mill

powered by water wheel at Tracays Farm

rhynd

mace

sealing plate

Castings made
by Lampitts
of Banbury

The cheek
bearings were
wood

3 taperheaded
adjusters

fixing plate

fixing bolts

outside
bearing

12"

design of the mechanical arrangements; a Watt beam engine powered the wood saws elsewhere on the estate.

The 16ft.-pitch back water-wheel of Traceys Farm, of wood and iron, is below ground level. The water is brought some distance from a storage pond through a brick-lined tunnel; the tail race is in a tunnel, too, some 20ft. below ground level. The iron lade and wheel are beginning to show serious decay, but the upright wooden shaft (driven by rim gear) and the crown wheel exist under a shelter. The farm machines have been scrapped, but I was able to rescue and restore a belt-driven corn mill with 32-in. peak stones, the metal work bearing the maker's name, Lampitts of Banbury.

Despite my predeliction for James Watt, I have since discovered that it was probably all the brain child of John Claudius Loudon, who managed the estate for a short period in the early 1800s. A man of many parts, he practised as an architect in London, was a noted botanist, and wrote widely on estate management, besides which he had a conviction that our southern farms should be like the Scottish border farms, with buildings surrounding a yard. He built the farm at Great Tew to demonstrate the advantages, including free water power (the water supply and feeder pond were actually an expensive project) and, as if he had no faith in local millwrights, he imported a young worker from Scotland named Lilley, which may explain the exotic back shot wheel and rim gear, normally foreign to Oxfordshire.

A water-wheel was installed to provide power to a Black Bourton farm (*not* Mill Farm), fed by a long canal carrying the Shill Brook. The undershot metal wheel remains driving through to shafting, but is no longer in use.

There was another unusual farm development in the part of north Berkshire ceded to the new Oxfordshire. Robert Campbell returned from Australia in 1859 a wealthy man, purchased the run-down Buscot Park estate, and proceeded to lavish money on it. He installed two water-wheel-driven pumps on the Thames to supply a 20-acre reservoir which was primarily for irrigation, but it also powered a turbine at Oldfield Farm and a second one for pumping water to the house.

Besides farming other ambitious manufacturing processes were planned, with a water-powered oil cake mill and an estate railway, but nothing prospered and a decade later all activity had ceased.

The paper-making trade was seeking to expand in the late 17th century. Paper was made of a watery mash with appropriate added fillers, which was all laboriously pounded by hand, each sheet skilfully made by lifting out some of the mash on a wire frame and leaving it to dry. A simple enough process when paper was in small demand, but as demand increased ways had to be sought to increase the production of the mash, and the abandoned fulling mills around the county were ideal for the task. Each sheet still needed individual skill, and more than a century passed before there was any attempt at the flow production of paper. The mills were well dispersed throughout the county:

Broughton, Deddington, Eynsham, Hampton Gay, Hazelford, Henley, North Newington, Sandford, Shiplake, Taynton (Upton), Widford, Wolvercote

and there were two mills in South Hinksey on the borders of Oxford City, but actually in Berkshire. Towle, a later owner of the mills, became mayor of Oxford; for a while he had a cardboard mill using the old waterworks premises at Folly Bridge.

Paper-making started at South Hinksey in 1675, and a little later at Wolvercote. Hampton Gay corn mill was adapted for paper in 1681, at which time there were 100 mills working in the whole of the country. Eynsham was working by 1682, producing best white paper when paper tended to be coarse; Hampton Gay was prospering, and Hutton, the owner, took over Adderbury Grounds corn mill and adapted it in 1684; a 10-year gap sees Sandford in production with corn milling, which continued till 1805.

Both Wolvercote and Eynsham claimed they were making the best white paper in England in 1718. One senses that the trade had its problems; Wolvercote was glad to restart corn milling 20 years later, yet within a few years (1743) they had installed a second pulveriser, which suggests a second water-wheel. Then Eynsham was burnt out. It was an unfortunate mill, suffering from disastrous fires, bankruptcies, and changes of ownership, but under its new owner, Jn. Brown, it was working again in 1761. The public was invited to compare the worth of an apprentice with a sheet of brown paper, for that was the reward offered at Hinksey for a runaway.

Wolvercote seems to have prospered and by 1796 had four pulverisers. Thos. Cobb of North Newington took out a patent for tinted paper, and even suggested it as a wall covering. At this time paper-making had started at Shiplake; Thos. Cobb, ever busy, made the first continuous paper-making machine, but did not bother to develop it. Meanwhile Fourdriniers of London had developed one of their own; nine were licensed out for use, and one came to Eynsham, and soon after that one came to Wolvercote. Eynsham started making waterproof tarred building paper which was 'highly praised'—possibly by J. C. Loudon of Great Tew who had thought it up. The year 1812 saw a Fourdrinier at Hampton Gay; Sandford was offered as a corn mill with two water-wheels and four pairs of French stones 'capable of being converted to paper making' and in 1823 Jas. Swann bought it for that purpose, employing 45 staff. Widford had a Fourdrinier by 1850; the industry was going through a bad time as paper-making materials were very scarce. Swann and Routlidge (Eynsham) succeeded in making paper from esparto grass, for which they received a Royal Award. They soon moved to the north where esparto grass was cheap, as it arrived in bulk as packing above iron ore cargoes from Spain, and Eynsham continued in some lesser capacity.

Adderbury Grounds was closed as being unprofitable in 1870, ironically when it was making bank note paper, and it was rebuilt and re-equipped for corn. Hampton Gay (same management) closed, too, but soon re-opened with steam auxiliary power. By 1880 Widford, Newington, Eynsham, and Hampton Hay had all ceased production, but Sandford prospered and had installed a Hercules turbine; available power was essential, and Shiplake abandoned the water-wheel and installed a steam engine.

Henley ceased in 1904 and soon so had Shiplake. The only survivors were the Hinksey mills and the large ones at Wolvercote and Sandford; here another turbine had been installed, the two producing 200 h.p. up to 1938. There is no trace of one of the Hercules, but the remaining one can be seen through the trash grid of the filled-in head race; there is a mysterious British Gilkes there, too, hidden away, which Kenneth Major says was a vertical-shafted 'Trent' (No. 1742) 120 h.p. on a 9ft. head.

Water power was used in Oxford for one rather special industrial process, that of brewing, and the pensioned-off water-wheel of early construction still exists at Morrell's Brewery, to be seen upstream from a nearby car park.

In 1716 an engineer named Aldersea, who had made a great name for himself supplying part of London with drinking water, was commissioned to provide 'a pumping engine' for the new Blenheim Palace. It consisted of two water-wheels working in adjacent streams on a common shaft, which was a three-throw crank; connecting rods actuated three rocking beams which drove pumps via rods at their ends. The pumps were gravity-fed from Fair Rosamund's Spring and delivered to storage tanks elsewhere. When Capability Brown caused the valley to be flooded, the apparatus had to be moved, and after a troubled life it found its fourth home in modified form alongside the corn mill in Old Woodstock. The three beams rocking about their centre became six shorter beams pivoted at their ends (grasshoppers), and each worked one pump. The original crank was copied and both cranks carried pinions which meshed at opposite sides of a pit wheel. Pumping ceased in about 1938; the water-wheel has gone, but the rest remains, rather shut away. Two water turbines installed at the bottom end of the lake in 1872 and 1890 still pump estate water. The severe drought in 1976 so lowered the level of the lake that the ground plan of an unexpected water mill was clearly revealed quite close to the mill, not working on the Glyme, but from a storage pond. It must have been abandoned when the valley was flooded in 1746.

A more ambitious water supply for Oxford was provided by a private company in 1694. The pumps were sited just below Folly bridge on what was the Berkshire shore. Contemporary documents describe it as an 'engine', but prints show plainly that there was an undershot water-wheel involved. The company did not prosper, and by 1730 Oxford Corporation had taken responsibility for financing it and then leasing it out to a series of unsuccessful entrepreneurs. The water was pumped through bored-out wooden pipes to an overhead tank in Market Street, then by gravity to a few who were prepared to pay for such a service.

That pumping station was abandoned in 1825 when Folly Bridge was rebuilt, so it operated for a full century. There had been improvements; the pumps had been replaced and a second (extra?) water-wheel had appeared in 1767, but a new installation on the north bank above the bridge provided opportunity for further improvement and for the rotting pipe work to be replaced. The new water-wheel by Easton and Amos was 15ft. in diameter and 6ft. wide, undershot, driving a pair of pumps. Demand slowly increased and a second pair of pumps, powered by a wheel 15ft. wide, were brought into use. Extreme high and low seasonal water levels had caused problems, so the new wheel was installed at a level higher than the first with paddles

Oxford's early waterworks; a print of 1772 shows the wheel enclosed.

30in. deep to cope with changing water levels; Easton and Amos were experienced water engineers, but this does seem a clumsy solution to the problem—the stroke of the pumps could be decreased at those times when power was inadequate.

'It was good enough for my old dad' was the motto which kept the many private wells in use, and only 200 premises had piped water. Nor can the well-users be blamed, for the river water was frankly unpalatable, tainted by the effluent from the new gas works just upstream and some unmentionable sewer outlets, besides the occasional unpleasantness washed down from Wolvercote Paper Mill. It even carried disease and it is small wonder that there were only 150 more 'on the mains' 25 years later. At last in 1852 public opinion prevailed and the waterworks committee seriously began to look for an alternative supply. About this time the new standard gauge railway was being built south to west of the city, and gravel extraction from the Hinksey meadows created a large lake of what proved to be good pure water. Here the new waterworks was built, powered by steam engines, and this installation was adequate till 1934. If the planners can be kept from it, the lake will continue to provide a delightful leisure area and bird-watching centre.

The abandoned water-wheels at the Folly Bridge pumphouse, not to be wasted, continued in use for the next 50 years, providing power for various trades.

Abingdon, too, had a water supply from 1696, pumped by water-wheel from the Thames on the east side of the river bridge, but the story of it is uncertain. At a later date, but before the assured supply from the Water Authority, two town gas-fuelled engines powered water pumps in the basement of the Town Hall; they have recently been restored as a piece of conservation.

There were lesser water undertakings operating in the county. The Town Mill at Burford was rebuilt and equipped with water pumps; so, too, was Charlbury Mill. For that matter there are still pumps working supplying farm needs, splashing away in hidden places on small streams, but because they continue to supply private drinking water I have omitted them from the gazetteer, and hope to keep their secret.

At one time in Little Clanfield district small farmers augmented their incomes by making straw rope. Hand-operated machines (thought to be of German origin) created a packing medium for breakable goods in the form of an inner core of straw-on-end wrapped round with a twisted straw binder. As farming prospered the machines were put aside, finally being gathered under one roof at Little Clanfield Mill, and a unique manufactory was created, the machines being adapted to take a belt drive from water-wheel powered shafting. This served up to 1940 when more reliable power was needed to make packing for the goods of war, and electricity was brought in. Production finally ceased about 1970, and the machines are no longer on the site. In the later years of peace the bonds were used to make archery targets, a nice contrast.

There must still be many who can recall the dim ages before the national grid spread its tentacles of electric power. Despite the romance of the kind and gentle oil lamps, I can vouch for their inconvenience, and it was small wonder that folks began to hanker for the rumoured magic of electric light. Mill owners were naturally resourceful people who knew about wheels and cogs, and how to transmit power, but dynamoes needed to turn at high speed and called for a sophistication of gearing which taxed even the mill engineer's ingenuity. Fluctuations in water flow called for a shed full of fickle stand-by batteries; it all might even prove more trouble than the despised oil lamps. Dismantled private systems can still be found with great, useless dynamos hiding in the shadows, ashamed of their impotence.

Though the small private installations may have been less than a success, there were some areas of the county adequately supplied by locally-formed electric light companies. A supply for Burford was generated by turbine in the lower mill; across the county at Crowmarsh a powerful wheel supplied current for a large area; a little further down river at Whitchurch a pair of wheels on the same shaft drove the generator. When Whitchurch and Crowmarsh worked as corn mills they might be seen as important, with two wheels for power and direct access to the river for bulk transport. Crowmarsh at least had an up-and-down life—in decay in the 1780s, rebuilt and employing 10 men a century later (including bone grinding), yet by 1906 so reduced that it failed to survive the flood damage of that time. Electric generators were installed in 1922, but all was derelict by 1930, and the mill spanning the water was demolished.

I know of three private generators still working by water power (one by turbine), but all of them take the easy way and are backed by a supply from the Electricity Authority. One of them is under threat of removal because of artificial changes in the river level; at least the other two get all the free hot water they need.

There seems at last to be an awareness that we have an energy crisis, and already there are firms prepared to supply a turbo-generator to any person sited near water who is able to meet the financial outlay; but before this can be readily undertaken there will need to be a revision of the Water Resources Act, which at present stultifies private effort. A National Association of Water Power Users has been formed to look after the immediate interests. It is all a far cry from the fulling stocks with which this chapter started.

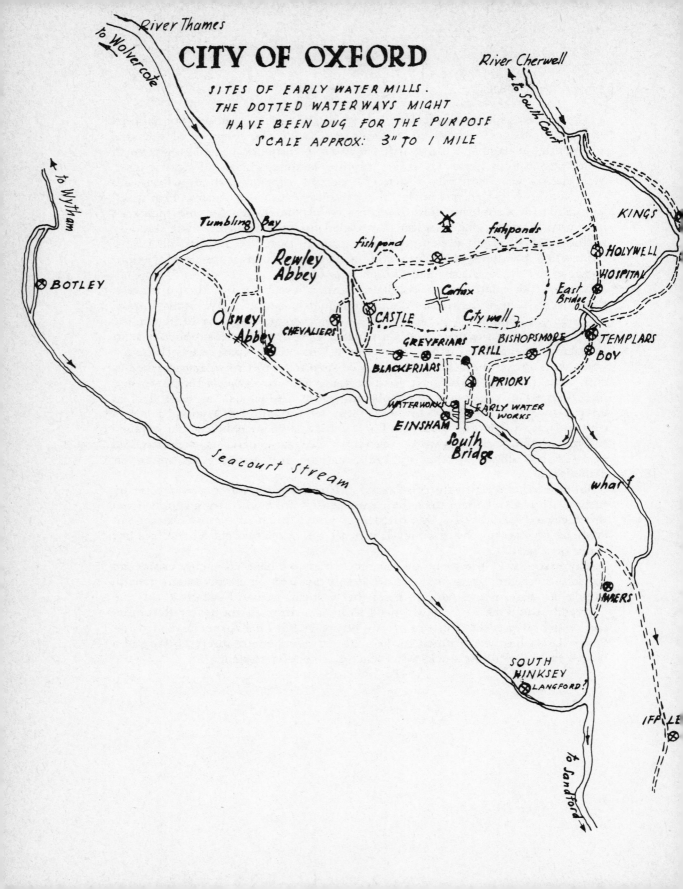

Chapter Six

THE CITY OF OXFORD

OXFORD WAS ALWAYS of some importance among the cities of England, with the tradition of learning established at an early date; with both Town and Gown in residence there was ever a need for corn mills to keep the busy city supplied with flour. There was little spare space within the city walls. One mill which subsequently became Castle Mills was set up at the immediate boundary, while some others (and there were many) were sited within the settlements established to the south and east. Osney to the west was presumably an 'own use' mill and there were some half dozen others available within reasonable distance whose main function was to serve outlying villages.

By the time King Charles arrived with his entourage in the 1600s far fewer mills were working, and they were hard put to keep all the extra people fed. Perhaps there was some difficulty, too, in getting grain in through the Cromwellian lines; some brave souls did manage to smuggle in the ingredients for gunpowder and that unstable mixture was compounded in the Castle Mills as part of their war effort, while a mint was set up to keep the coffers full.

In 1790 and 1850 abortive schemes were mooted to widen Seacourt Stream, removing the mills thereon and bringing the main flow of the river through the cleared channel. Winters came as uncomfortably as ever until the late 19th century, when at last it was realised that the constricting gap down river at Sandford was the culprit; a new weir and by-pass channel there, coupled with other aspects of water control, now provide the less threatening situation that we enjoy today, though it did mean Sandford Mill giving up all water rights in 1938.

There had been a bad record of flooding up to this time. In the 1800s, when the new Magdalen Bridge was being built, the water lapped the roadway there, which meant a rise of 18 feet; the weirs were choked at Castle Mills, and the water was forced uncontrollably through the mill, displacing a heavy metal water-wheel newly installed. The miller and his family at Botley were marooned in the attic, all the city mills had moved their easily-spoiled goods hopefully to the upper floors, and Cassington, well upstream on the Thames, was flooded out.

Three mills only were listed as taxable in the Domesday List. Others existed at that time as the following will show, but the early dates are uncertain.

Castle Mills, sometimes Kings Mills. There is no doubt about the site for the rush of water can still be seen under the shadow of St George's Tower, the surviving part of the Castle. The waters, conveniently dammed by the Saxons, made it a simple matter to fill the moat and may have influenced the siting of the Castle. Robert D'Oiley, finally reformed and set to good works, gave the mill to Osney Abbey in 1129. It came into the hands of King Stephen by forfeiture in 1140 and maybe it was his kindly Queen Maud who persuaded him to rent it to Mr Cheney, the mayor.

The mill figures in a long series of benevolences. King John (1199–1216) gave one half of the mill to the Burgesses, 'the other half the Queen Mother holdeth', which makes it clear that there were two water-wheels. In 1230 Henry III granted his share to Godfrey of Crancombe, and Edward III (1327–1377) let his to Richard Foster.

Richard II (1377–1399) gave the whole mill to Osney Abbey and it was held by them up to the Dissolution, though not without constant protest from the city burgesses, who for some reason thought they had a better right. In 1542 Henry VIII made over his share to the Bishop of Oxford and still the burgesses were complaining; by some devious means they had acquired the lot by 1591. As businessmen they succeeded, for they soon put in another wheel and stones, and by 1690 they needed another one. Court records show that they were very strict to protect their socage rights, but the same records show them being prosecuted when they were often caught extracting more than the miller's share.

Though well placed for business Castle Mills never caught up with roller milling developments and spent the declining years on any tasks where a bit of cheap power was needed; the buildings survived in some form till 1932, out-of-date, ill-used, and in the way.

King's Mill, sometimes Queens Mill, was reasonably near the City at the downstream end of Mesopotamia—a scholarly reference to the 'land between two rivers' which had been formed when the mill-stream was dug. This was a Domesday site listed as being in Headington parish. In 1260 Henry III is supposed to have given the mill to the Hospital of St John, but a document dated 1467 shows that it was (again?) granted to the Master and Brethren of the Hospital of St John by Magdalen College. The Brethren disbanded in 1476 and the mill came back to Magdalen, who then swopped it with Merton College for some unspecified property. Milling ceased in 1825, but cottage-like buildings still exist and the head race is well maintained.

Holywell Mill. An old site claiming socage rights. It continued in use till the late 19th century. It was owned jointly by Osney Abbey and a private person. When Merton College was established it received both shares (1264) which were sold to Magdalen in 1888; they own the private house which now spans the stream and are responsible for the adjacent sluice.

Hospital Mill. Magdalen College built this mill solely for the domestic use of St John's Hospital, but it was judged to interfere with the run of the tail water of Holywell Mill, who had prior rights, and it was demolished in 1486.

Templars Mill was sited on the south of the east bridge and was shown to be in Cowley parish in the Domesday List. In 1146 Maud, wife of King Stephen, gave it to the Knight Templars of Cowley. The last record is in 1350.

Boy Mill stood a little down river from Templars and was listed, too, in Cowley parish. It belonged to the Canons of St Frideswides, but by 1122 Roger, Bishop of Sarum, had got his hands on it. He gave it to Godstow Nunnery on its foundation in 1137, and it was handed back to St Frideswides (possibly under duress) in 1358.

Bishopsmore Mill was situated in Christchurch Meadow (The Shire Lake). It had the same early history as Boy Mill and again the Bishop of Sarum's generosity was frowned upon by Henry I who ordered him in 1122 to restore it to St Frideswide's. He failed to do so and in 1139 both the King and the Archbishop of Canterbury were after him. The story ends unfulfilled in 1156.

Black Friars was a double mill immediately south of the city and was originally owned by Henry III. He gave it to the Bishop of Carlisle in 1246, who in turn gave it to the Black Friars, hence the name.

Trill Mill stood on a stream to the south which was no doubt specially dug, being fed from the Ald Weir, which was established across the main Thames. It was given to St Frideswide's by Benedict Keepharme in 1180. The stream was 20ft. wide, but became hopelessly fouled by bones and offal dumped from the shambles in Pembroke Street. The nuisance abated when the slaughterhouse was moved to a site to the south of the Grand Pont.

Ald Weir was overthrown in 1550, which must mark the end of milling, and the once busy mill stream is now a furtive dribble mostly confined in a tunnel. A grindstone preserved in the Memorial Gardens is not from a corn mill, but is an edge runner stone and maybe was rescued from nearby Grandpont Mill (The Water Works), where it might have been part of some industrial process.

There was a waterway running from Trill Mill Stream southward into the Thames. Bakers and brewers took water from it, but it was tainted and caused much illness in the city and eventually public opinion caused it to be filled in. Recent excavations reveal confusing traces of waterways in this area, some running west to east.

Priory Mill worked downstream from Trill Mill and may well have had the same history, but no records appear.

Grey Friars Mill. The Friars erected this mill upstream of Trill Mill, whereupon the greedy owners of Castle Mills complained that it interfered with their working. Being below a downstream weir that was surely unjust, and despite their protests the mill remained in use until the dissolution of the monastery.

Einsham Mill was a double mill just above the South Bridge. It existed before 1066 and the name suggests that it belonged to Eynsham Abbey. It must have been in the way of Robert D'Oiley's bridge building, for there is no record of it after 1109.

Langford Mill existed before 1066, described as being 'by Oxford Bridge'. It may have been sited on one of the many waterways in the vicinity of the South Bridge, and if so it survived demolition when the bridge was rebuilt, for in the 12th century it was the gift of Wm. de Seacourt to Abingdon Abbey. It was more likely to have been a mill further south of the city later to become a paper mill, sited on the Seacourt Stream.

Chevaliers Mill was on a small stream probably specially dug to the west of the castle. It was given to the Knight Templars by King Stephen's Maud. Castle Mills claimed that it robbed them of water and Castle Mills always won, so it probably became a horse-driven mill, as the name suggests.

With so many mills in one close area needing a head and a flow of water it is no wonder that there were wrangles. In 1337 a rabble from Binsey, Medley and Osney, incensed by the constant flooding, smashed the sluices and weirs at Castle Mills, who for once lost out.

There was a Horsemill Lane, in the Merton Street area, which suggests another horse-driven mill. A water-mill of some provenance was thought to be sited outside the North Gate—there was a stream there which by a contemporary report 'ran deep and clear' through a series of fish ponds.

Osney Mill was built soon after the foundation of the Abbey in 1129. We shall never know how many waterways were dug in this area, certainly two other mills (one for fulling) were established soon afterwards. The main river course was at this time further west and what now appears to be the main stream is misleading, being the original small mill stream considerably enlarged by later river works to establish it as the main navigation.

Yet another mill was established at Osney in the 1200s, and this made such a final complication of waterways that serious malfunction of the sewers resulted. The Supervisors of Sewers for the city insisted that this hold-up be removed.

There are no references to milling at Rewley Abbey. They may have used Cassington, which they owned. Perhaps there were plans for an Abbey Mill when they built a weir across the Thames of such magnitude that it impeded Osney's water and that meant a lawsuit to settle the matter. Some archaic words used to describe mill waterways were melesille, foresille, tailsille, and tumblyngbay—could the present Tumbling Bay bathing place be the site of Rewley's water poaching?

With Holywell and Castle Mills so determined about their sokage rights, it is surprising that so many mills managed to keep in work. Moreover, with the whole area flowing with water it is surprising that there were windmills.

The two fairly adjacent mills and one other nearby on the high ground at Headington perhaps were justified, as there was only one small brook to feed Bayswater ponds, but the one at the top of St Giles might seem to be an intruder. A Holywell Parish Terrier map of 1660 (Merton College Library) shows a typical post mill at the north end of St Giles; the site was perpetuated by Windmill Inn and Windmill Yard up to the end of the 19th century.

The main southerly course of the Thames away from the city passed originally through the present Long Bridges bathing place and on to what is now a complication of weirs for flood control. This marks the site where one of the paper mills stood, after which the river then found its way onwards to the south of Iffley Mill. It is probable that the original mill stream was an extension of the Cherwell, and the presence of a commercial wharf at one time at the bottom of Jackdaw Lane does suggest that it was navigable at least up to that point. The digging out of the New Cut over the course of Iffley Mill stream in 1771 was one of the biggest pieces of water management done around Oxford; the old tortuous course of the river was not an easy journey for the barge captains, just regaining composure after jiggling their clumsy craft through the waterways of Folly Bridge, and the New Cut immediately became the favoured route for commercial vessels. This was much to the profit of the Iffley millers, who owned the water rights and could charge a toll. They eventually sold those rights to the Thames Conservancy for £500 in 1866.

Now we are left with a mess of weirs, lashers, and locks, all resulting from man's efforts to harness the water, and dating right back to the time the little community established itself on the flood-threatened gravel spine.

NOTE.—Since writing this chapter Volume IV of the *Victoria County History of Oxfordshire* has been published, to which I humbly refer my more academic readers.

Appendix to Chapter Six

In 1880 W. H. Turner had access to some City Records which have since been lost. He published them in book form and these are mill references extracted therefrom:

25 Sept. 1525: 'It is ordered that the bailiffs for the year of their entering, Rich. Cotton and Wm. Archer, shall pay £6 and every bailey £3 for the repair of the Castle Mills, long in decay. To be repaid again the next 20s. and every bailey 10s. And every bailey in time come that shall be admitted shall pay 1s. for laidylling of mill, making of flood gates and banks and conducting water to the mill, making spindle, mill picks, millers wages as is the old custom, and all other charges.'

26 Sept. 1527: 'Jn. Snow and Thos. Walker to have 3s. 4d. each for labour in repairing the town share of the Mills'.

4 June 1546: John Lewis took the bailiffs to court, claiming that they had taken too much tollage. They were ordered to hand back the three quarters overcharged, also money in lieu of what had previously been overcharged, the worth of four quarters at 23s. 4d. per quarter. He was to have the key to the mill and have sole use two days a week using a nominated miller, the bailiffs taking the prescribed tollage under the eyes of Lewis or his deputy.

16 Sept. 1549: 'Henceforth the bailiffs shall not have half of the mills, but the City. Instead the bailiffs shall have a payment of £20 paid twice yearly by the key keepers. The bailiffs will no longer have to pay Oriel College £19 and the City will pay till the fee ferme is discharged'.

29 Sept. 1549: Wm. Tylcoke, late a bailiff, paid the chamberlain £10 in part payment of the fee ferme. Jn. Hore and Jn. Simpson were discharged from the office of chamberlain and bailiff on payments of £6 and £6 8s. 4d. to the use of the City.

12 April 1557: 'Agreed that the Bishop of Oxford shall enter into the moyte of the Castle Mills, paying £7 down and half the charges for the impliments of the mill and putting up sufficient surety'.

6 Oct. 1558: 'The waters belonging to the Castle Mills to be let to Alderman Williams, Mr. Elmes and Edges for one year'.

8 Jan. 1559: 'Both bakers and citizens shall grind all their bread corn at Castle Mills according to the old custom and forfeit all corn ground elsewhere, divided between bailiff and body of town'.

22 June 1568: The same announcement 'with no possible chance of retaliation' added.

1567: Pd. Mr. Waite for millstones   £15
    for delivery   £3 6s. 8d.

22 November 1568: 'White or brown bakers or brewers shall forfeit even the sacks if caught grinding elsewhere, half to the City and the other half to the bailiff who catches him'.

29 Dec. 1568: The same announcement but 'it will cost the carrier £10 and prison till he pays'.

3 May 1569: 'Mr. Lewis shall have licence to grind 24 qrs. weekly at Castle Mills, otherwise Queens Mills during his life'.

14 Aug. 1571: Wm. Furniss warned not to grind elsewhere or forfeit half to her Majesty and half to the City.

5 Oct. 1571: 'All freemen, all bakers, and all else shall grind at the Castle Mills unless permit obtained from stewards of mill, or forfeit half to the City, half to the taker, with no redress'.

2 Nov. 1571: Thos. Smith, brewer, to provide two load horses to carry flour for bakers and freemen, to be paid £4 per year in two payments, the City to provide stable and shoeing.

12 Sept. 1572: Thos. Attwood fined £10 for carrying his corn and that of others to Osney Mills—after an apology he got his money back.

16 Oct. 1572: Eleven bakers paid an average of 4s. per year towards the mill horse.

5 Oct. 1582: Mr. Cox confessed that he had ground corn otherwise than at Kings Mills and must show cause why he should not pay £10.

Over those years the following tradesmen had been granted the freedom of the City:

1531   Thos. Foster, fuller; Alex. Baker, Thos. Hoplins, millers.
1539   Thos. a Medley, fuller.
1552   Thos. Attwood, fuller.
1559   Christopher Leryns, fuller.
1561   Rich. Haynes, miller.
1566   Francis Jennings, miller.
1568   Mark Wicks, apprentice fuller.
1580   Thos. Hartley, apprentice fuller.

After the respect paid by the City to those tradesmen it is amusing to learn that by the 1890s the drivers of Oxford's horse trams were instructed to refuse to carry 'a sweep in his dirt, a miller in his dust'.

Chapter Seven

WINDMILLS

ON A LOCAL RADIO PROGRAMME which was supposed to be about water-mills I was casually asked about windmills, and I hazarded a guess that there had been 'a dozen or so' in the county. I was taken to task about my estimate by a local historian, so we both solemnly counted on our fingers those mills we could recall, and agreed at fifteen. I was so concerned with water-mills that I had overlooked all the information that had appeared on documents and maps relating to windmills, nor had I been much encouraged by the mill books written at national level, for they had generally ignored Oxfordshire mills.

It was suggested that I should publish my water-mill findings and that also I ought to write a bit about windmills, as a sort of postscript, and it was from such a small beginning that I uncovered over sixty sites—sites being the operative word, as most of the mills existed solely in documents or as symbols on older maps. We did not have many windmills, for this area has a weather record of unpredictable winds and long periods of calm, but, in fact, the map reveals a pattern of mills to the north-west and east, where the terrain generated localised winds.

As far as is known there were no windmills in the Domesday List; the first safe date recorded for a windmill is a late 12th-century one, and that was not local, but an early 13th-century mill was recorded near Chinnor. Mills are noted at Beckley and Bicester a little later in that century, and others in the early 14th century at Garsington, Headington, Henton, Wain Hill. There are several bits of high ground in the county which appear on maps as Windmill Hill; can we think of them as old sites, for there is nothing to show today; equally there are plenty of known sites with no evidence remaining.

The mills which have survived in some form are Great Haseley, whose future is secured by the private owner; Wheatley, where restoration work is in progress; a bare tower standing at Blackthorn; North Leigh, where decay is rampant and the future hopeless; and the tower forming part of a house conversion at Wardington.

To remind us of some of the mills (both wind and water) which did exist an unexpected bonus turned up in, of all places, the Museum of Scientific

Instruments in Broad Street, Oxford. In their library there exists an album of photographs taken by a Mr Underhill around 1900. He wrote on the flyleaf of the need to record the mills before they disappeared, and we can be glad he did so. There is yet another windmill hidden away at Bloxham Grove, of which more later, and apart from the latter, I will explain that these few have survived because of their method of construction—in fact, because they are tower mills.

The **Post Mill** was the first type, a box-like structure (the *Buck*) freely pivoting on a central supporting post, which was either set in the ground or more properly supported by four angled struts whose lower ends were set on an interlocking cross frame of wood; the whole structure was called a *Trestle*. The drawings of the little mill at Bloxham show exactly how the four-quarters post trestle was arranged, but there were exceptions to this design, with three interlocking cross-trees and six quarter bars. Three of these mills were local: Chinnor, which is shown on a drawing; Stokenchurch (once in Oxon.) and Bledlow (just over the border). Though charred by fire and lightning, the old windshaft at Wheatley will be fit for re-use; it is undoubtedly part of a previous mill, and if the main post of the mill is indeed that from the site burnt down in 1767, then the mortices cut into it suggest that the trestle was a three-cross type.

In *English Historic Carpentry* (1980) Cecil Hewett shows the remarkable skills of the carpenters who were working when the form of the post mill was first established; regrettably such skill did not pass into the framing of the bucks, though beautifully made intricate joints frequently appear in trestles.

The bucks were heavy and may appear cumbersome, but they were well balanced and could be pivoted around to get the sails into the wind, the wide shallow access 'ladder' being slightly lifted and then used as a lever to move the buck, perhaps with a cartwheel mounted at the bottom to facilitate this. A close-fitting wooden ring steadied the buck on the post; perhaps even wooden rollers at that point made turning easier. The drawings of Bloxham show the main features of the buck, perhaps somewhat miniaturised. Bigger bucks, in need of better support, turned on rollers running on a ring supported from the trestle, and this may well have been the reason for the six-quarter bar design.

The next step in development was the **Smock** mill; the body was built from the ground up as non-moving, and the *cap* only was moveable, to turn the sails into the wind. The illustration of the main frames of the cap shows long mortices to allow adjustment of the sprattle and tail beams, wedges being used to secure them when the final position was decided. It must have been an important routine task to keep those wedges tight, especially as the large unbraced rectangle might rhomboid—metal struts and braces which look like later additions support that idea. There were a few lower courses of

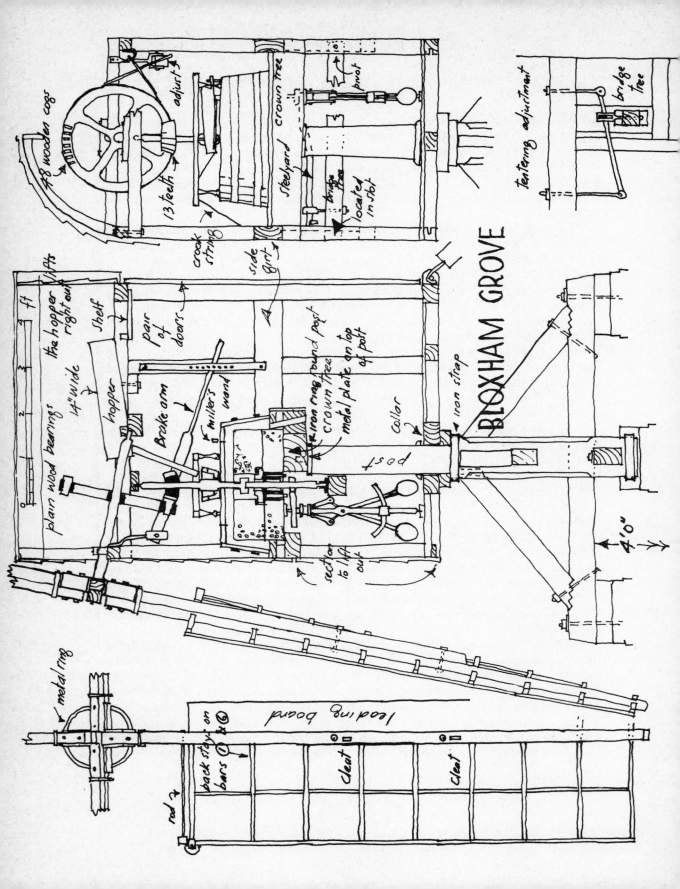

BLOXHAM GROVE

48 wooden cogs

13 teeth

adjust

crook string

side girt

crown tree

steelyard

bridge tree

located in slot

pivot

bridge tree

tentering adjustment

the hopper right out

1/4 ft

4 ft

shelf

14" wide

hopper

plain wood bearings

pair of doors

Brake arm

miller's wand

iron ring round post

crown tree

metal plate on top of post

collar

post

iron strap

section to lift out

4'0"

metal ring

rod

back stay on bars ① & ⑥

leading board

cleat

cleat

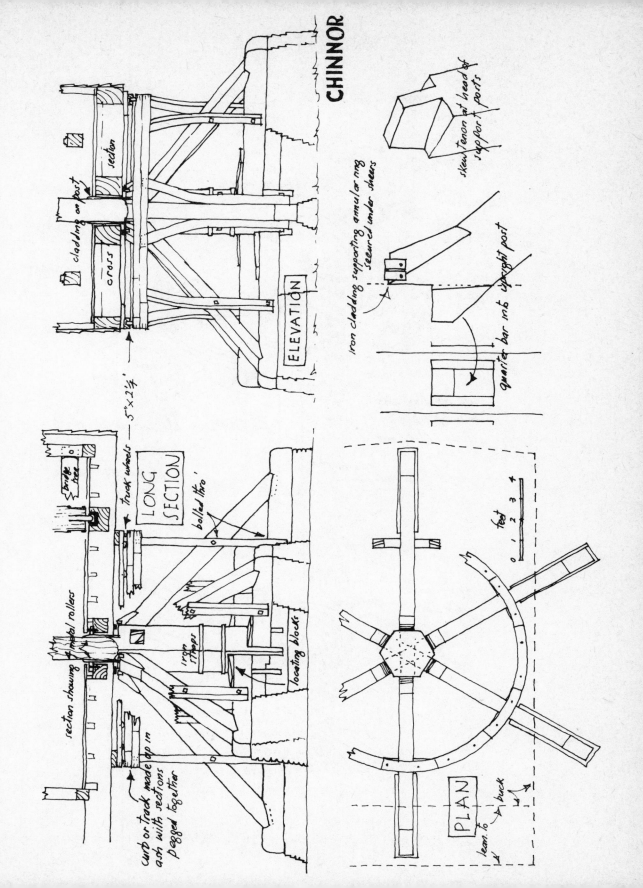

CHINNOR

cladding on post

section

cross

ELEVATION

skew tenon at head of support posts

iron cladding supporting annular ring secured under sheers

quarter bar into upright post

section showing metal rollers

bridge tree

Truck wheels — 5" × 2½'

LONG SECTION

bolted thro'

iron straps

locating blocks

curb or track made up in ash with sections pegged together

PLAN

lean to

buck

feet
0 1 2 3 4

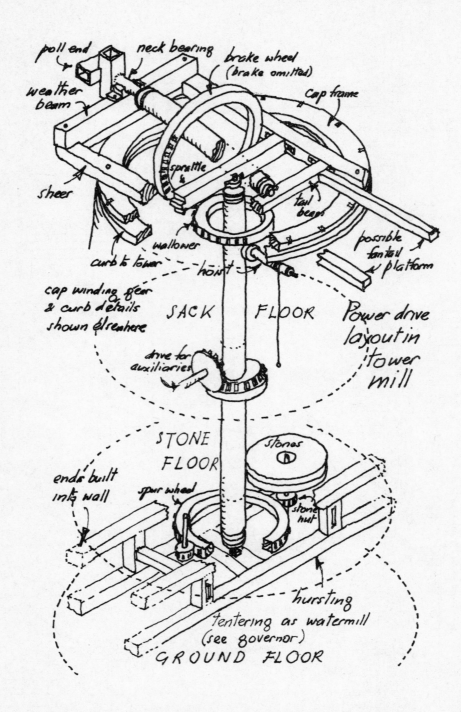

poll end
neck bearing
brake wheel
(brake omitted)
weather beam
cap frame
sheer
sprattle
tail beam
wallower
curb to tower
possible fantail platform
hoist
cap winding gear & curb details shown elsewhere
SACK   FLOOR
Power drive layout in tower mill
drive for auxiliaries
STONE FLOOR
Stones
ends built into wall
spur wheel
stone hut
hursting
tentering as watermill (see governor)
GROUND FLOOR

The arrangement of both smock and tower mills

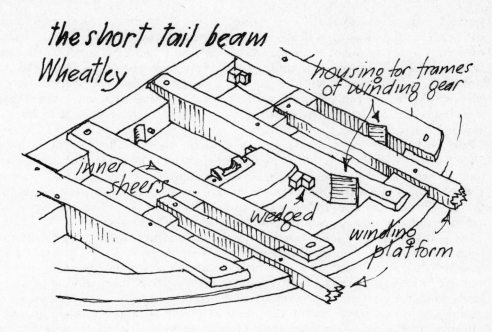

the short tail beam
Wheatley

housing for frames
of winding gear

inner
sheers

wedged

winding
platform

masonry or brickwork as foundation to the smock mill, and the tower
(usually octagonal) was timber framed and originally covered with thatch.
Did the shape suggest a man in a smock? As fine cut boarding became
available, that was used and a white painted mill was a beautiful sight, as the
local example at Nettlebed shows.

Being made of wood, post and smock mills were particularly at risk from
fire, so the arrival of the Tower mill was not unexpected, with the complete
tower a solid structure of brick or stone (the reason why our few mills
survived), with the same timber-framed cap as the smock mill. The tower
was usually built to a round plan, which makes the octagonal plan at Wheatley
of interest. Perhaps the local masons, of great repute, considered a round
tower no demand on their skills.

The early covering of the cap was likely to have been thatch but in the
Chiltern vale there was a later tradition of graceful ogee caps covered in sheet
copper with an ornamental finial; unfortunately the valuable copper has
proved a challenging target for vandals. Outside the vale we must admit to less
elegant shapes, some hemi-spherical like the tops of modern silos, some like
lumpy, upturned boats.

The small mill at Bloxham Grove had been the subject of much conjecture
until Arthur Smith, who does mill research, rediscovered the story. It was
built one-third size as late as 1865 (which explains its survival) by Henry

Warriner, whose family held the estate; it was a whimsical memorial to all past millers, but was practical, too, and served the nearby farm. Henry Warriner was an engineer with Maudsley, Son and Field of London. He also installed a steam-driven corn mill at the farm (the engine by Lampitts of Banbury), but his startling success was a steam-driven boat shaped like a swan which ran on the Oxford Canal. The windmill has suffered some recent storm damage, but restoration is in train—to this end I have done a measured drawing.

Post and smock mills, being earlier in date, were built as small as mills tended to be, with little or no storage, and they had the same problems when trade increased. At post mills storage was contrived by enclosing the trestle (a *Roundhouse*). By the time the tower mills were being built, the needs for storage were understood and an extra upper floor was provided, but we never had the giant commercial windmills found elsewhere in England.

Local mills were of such height that the extremities of the sails swept the ground, creating an area of danger best avoided—there was the choice of two opposite doors for safety; at Wheatley and Haseley there were even two opposite fireplaces to cope with wayward winds. Blackthorn Mill appears to stand on a tump, but it is revealed that after the tower was built on level ground earth was piled round the base; in effect an area to tend the sails. Standing in the doorway the startled visitor finds himself looking into a cellar, the joists and flooring long decayed. Haseley is raised in the same manner, but only a few feet.

'Tump' is the word used for an artificial mound on which a mill is built to gain some elevation. A few remain in some form; those at Studley and Salford have eroded into mere heaps. There is an interesting heap on the Kop at South Weston which supports the story that a mill once stood there and was moved to Wendover. Charlton tump did war service, being hollowed out for an air raid shelter.

When you see a post mill isolated upon piers you can appreciate what self-contained structures they were. If a miller was not satisfied that he was getting his worth from the wind he might set about lifting the base frame, corner by corner, building up the piers course by course till he could see the sails were up where the wind blew usefully.

Mills were sometimes moved bodily. There are stories from other counties of great teams of oxen steadfastly hauling post mills on sledges across country. We have on record the shifting of a smock mill in 1823 from Watlington to a windier site at Nettlebed, some five miles, but this was done on a timber wagon, normally used to shift tree trunks. Rex Wailes suggests that Chinnor Mill was brought from Chatham. If so, it is a much-travelled mill. In 1967 the site of the mill was coveted for building land, and the developer sold the mill carcase to an enthusiast on a chance visit, which he carried off to Essex and safely stored. It now seems likely that the mill will be brought back and reinstated by the Chiltern Society, cheering news and more travelling—could this be the same mill that was once moved from Slough to Chatham? The early windmills, being small, had no real need for tackle to lift the sacks of grain—tackle is a word describing anything provided to do a task. In the Thame millwrights' journals I have quoted he writes 'took tackle to mill', a tantalising reference to all the tools and pulleys and so on he would need for his work, which, incidentally, he often transported on a donkey cart. Before the B.B.C. undermined the local dialect, 'tackle' was possibly reflected by 'how does it ackle', or 'does it ackle alright', when expressing concern about the behaviour of faulty mechanisms.

To get back to the sack tackle. In a windmill there are plenty of turning shafts so I don't doubt that the slack-belt type of hoist was used. It happens that the only two mills left to examine made use of a different type. The wallower which brings the drive in on a water-mill is down on the wheel

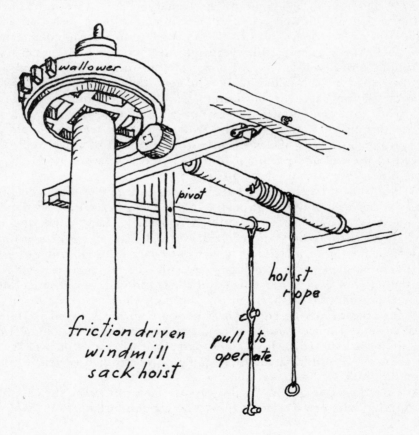

shaft; in a windmill it is away up top of the upright
shaft. On its underside the wallower presents a
flat surface against which the hoist can be driven
by friction. It is the same gentle action as the slack
belt and its application made by a similar manual
control. The hoist at Chinnor was gear-driven
from the wind-shaft. I found the windlass at
Haseley lying on the sack floor and its method
of application could only be guessed at—it was

driven through a Hooke's joint and another such joint was used elsewhere on
some shafting. The Rev. Hooke spent some of his 17th-century ministry
inventing, and he produced this simple universal joint to transmit a drive
through an angle.

To provide some control if erratic winds threatened to produce erratic
grinding speeds it was usual to fit governors, which would provide automatic
control. The two surviving are of the same type, driven from the upright shaft.
If the action is followed on the illustration it will be seen that a rise in sail
speed will cause the action of the bob weights to lift the collar, and through
devious linkages (steelyard/breyer/bridge-tree) lower the runner stones; this
in simple terms will act like a brake on the turning gear. Hand adjustment
was available for the miller to set the tentering at what he judged would be
a norm for the day. The blacksmith who made Wheatley governor made use
of a heavy stone spindle to form the upright spindle to the governor.

The turning of a buck into the wind may have seemed simple enough; it
was not such an easy job with the cap of a smock or tower mill. Long poles
stayed to the cap and reaching toward ground level were used (*tail poles*), but
mechanisms were also used for the job.

At Milton and Blackthorn a long hand chain running round a deeply recessed
pulley at cap level powered through to a drive which was a toothed cog engaging
with cogs set round inside the curb. At Wheatley a hand crank operated at cap
level through the same type of gear. North Leigh, where proper examination
is denied, has more archaic gear; a hand chain is used, and the drive finally
reaches a wooden worm which engages with cogs set round outside the tower—
the shelter roof over it has fallen and the worm will soon disintegrate. Haseley
enjoyed automation in the form of a tail fan which powered through to a cog
engaging cogs inside the curb. These cogs are normally wooden. Here they had
decayed and sections had been replaced by iron cogs cast in sections of 15
and spiked to the curb. In the photograph of Chinnor you will see a type of
fan alien to Oxfordshire, the drive going down through wheels in contact with
a circular track set on the ground.

The previous paragraph explains various ways of turning the cap, but not the
relationship between cap and tower. The cap, windshaft, brake wheel and sails

will weigh several tons; in fact, it is the weight which 'holds it down' and it is this weight which has to be moved. The original method was so simple as to be unbelievable: a curb of substantial wood formed the top of the tower, a similar ring provided the foundation of the cap, and these two were in direct contact, perhaps optimistically smeared with tallow, and the name *dead curb* suggests its reluctant movement. To maintain the cap centrally on

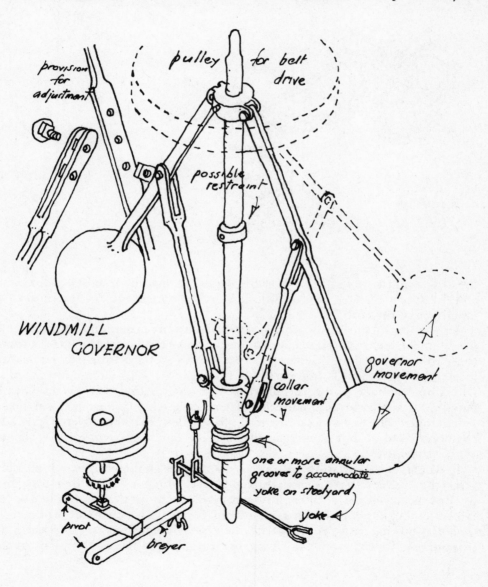

provision for adjustment

pulley for belt drive

possible restraint

WINDMILL GOVERNOR

governor movement

collar movement

one or more annular grooves to accommodate yoke on steelyard

yoke

pivot

breyer

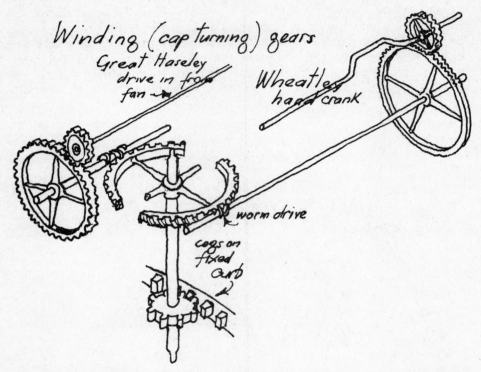

Winding (cap turning) gears
Great Haseley drive in from fan →
Wheatley hand crank
worm drive
cogs on fixed curb ↓

the tower and to resist the thrust of the sails a variable number of horizontal wheels (*truck wheels*) were positioned on the cap frame to bear against the inner face of the curb.

The action of the dead curb was improved by the provision of *trolley wheels* to the underside of the cap frame—a *live curb*. A final improvement was to have the curb and cap frame separated by a ring of wood into which wheels were located at intervals (a *shot curb*). It is a type used in later mills fitted out with foundry-made ironwork, but it is surprising to find it in the much earlier dated mills at Haseley and Wheatley. There are further refinements at Wheatley —the trolley wheels ran in a cast-iron channel and they are tapered; nowadays engineers would call it a tapered roller bearing, and it is a very early application of the principle.

It would be speculation on my part to write about early windmill sails. I refer the reader to a modestly-priced *Source Book of wind and watermills*, by Rex Wailes. Late 19th-century photographs show that generally the local millers could not afford the type of sail fitted with adjustable wooden slats (*patents*) but had to be content with the type with cloths secured to sail frames (*commons*). Indeed, some in their poverty managed with only a pair of sails, the companion pair lost through damage or decay. A rough canvas was normally used for sail cloths; at Wheatley (where everything seems to have happened) they used coarse hessian-like material woven at nine threads to the inch.

The cannister box (poll end) at Wheatley bears the date 'Eagle Foundry 1784'. I hoped it was traceable to a local foundry of that name, but I found that they did not have that casting capacity till 1810. It would be interesting to know how that heavy lump of metal was brought to the site, and from what distance. Gibbins of Great Haseley did work on their local mill and the dated work (1889) presumably indicates a refit—winding gear, curb cogs and iron windshaft.

It was a slow process getting common sails ready for work each day. Each sail had to be brought round and held on the brake while the cloth was set to suit the judged wind strength; the miller needed to be well informed about local weather portents. When he was busy and storm winds threatened he had to be prepared to keep the mill working to the limit, finally turning the sails out of the wind, stopping them one by one, and getting the straining canvas off at the last critical moment.

The brake was a necessity, but, considering what a threat its use was to the mill's safety, it is amazing it was not improved until ironwork came into use. The action was a wooden band clamped round the wooden brake wheel and everyone knows that wood and friction soon produce fire—*Imperial Magazine* reported in 1760 'near Winslow five wind mills were burnt to the ground during the gale'. A pull on the hand rope would release the securing pawl and allow the heavy brake arm to fall and apply the brake; to release the brake a second

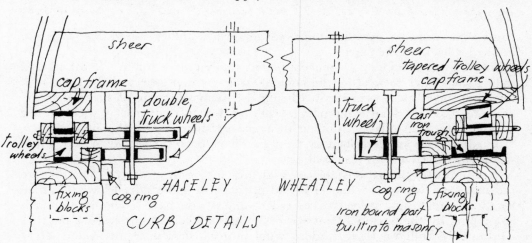

sail cloth settings

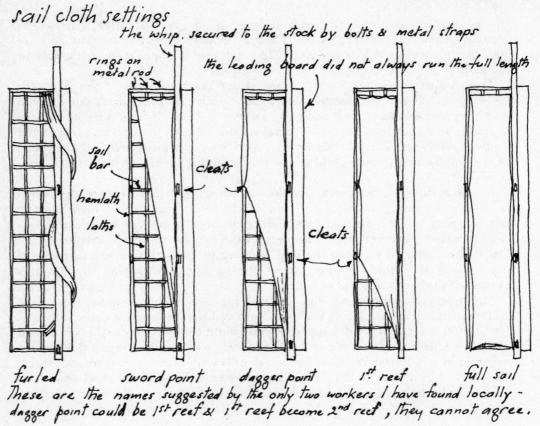

the whip. secured to the stock by bolts & metal straps

rings on
metal rod

the leading board did not always run the full length

sail
bar

cleats

hemlath

laths

cleats

furled   sword point   dagger point   1st reef   full sail
These are the names suggested by the only two workers I have found locally -
dagger point could be 1st reef & 1st reef become 2nd reef, they cannot agree.

hand rope working through some advantageous pullies raised the arm and
hooked it back on the pawl.

The life of a miller is often compared to that of a sailor. Windmills and
sailing ships have to weather the same hazards; another aspect is that they both
might be investment ventures with ruin the likely outcome of storm damage.
Ongoing leases of some windmills reveal that they were owned by small groups
of men who can only be thought of as having their eye on the main chance,
even when they are described as 'Gent'; to have been the tenant of such a mill
would have been a great responsiblity.

A continued threat was lightning strike, for some parts of the mill are
inevitably up where the danger is and difficult to make safe. I have just read
an article 'Lightning never strikes twice—unless you have a windmill', and it
is a report by the National Centre for Alternative Technology showing nature's
continued assault on their modern wind motors, despite sophisticated safety
precautions. A visit to the Centre (just north of Machynlleth in Wales) can be

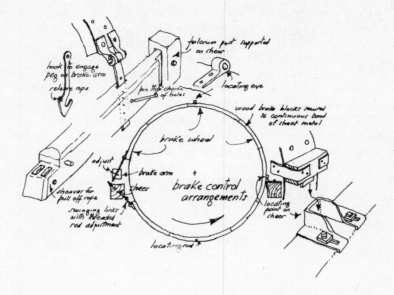

rewarding; besides many examples of energy conservation, the actual production of energy by wind and water power is demonstrated, giving the opportunity to see the form future wind generators might take.

In 'Applied Power' I have written of the industrial tasks in which water-mills engaged themselves, generally tasks in which an actual flow of water was an advantage. Three windmills, Wheatley and Milton (tower mills), and the strange mill at South Weston, found work other than milling by grinding ochre. The local source of ochre was once quite important and was even exported; it is an earth-like substance which provided a colour base for dyes and paints—naturally pale yellow, but if burned in a kiln (both tower mills had one) a red is produced. The grinding was done outside the mills with edge-runner stone grinders driven by belt from a vertical shaft driven from the spur. It was probably done on a contract basis for those firms who dug up the raw material (The Liberator Co. and Sennett Roper are two names discovered).

The story of the decline of wind-milling in this county is much the same as the decline of water-milling. Perhaps it came a little earlier, mainly because the wooden buildings were much more at risk, and if gales had not already done so it became prudent to demolish both tower and post mills. The remains provided a useful source of stone and firewood.

Caps of the surviving tower mills developed leaks which encouraged localised decay, and photographs exist which show the mills surviving, limping on with only one pair of sails and unsightly roofing sheets nailed over the holes. After such a sad end it is pleasant to think that some spent their last years with honour, serving as look-out posts for the Home Guard.

Besides the occasional restored windmill, which most people regard as a romantic and acceptable part of the landscape, there are likely to be other strange intruders, as the recent H.M.S.O. report on alternative wind sources of energy shows. They admit that there may be possible environmental issues in those areas chosen for development, but they are likely to be in remote Scotland and on some off-shore sites; meanwhile Oxfordshire, with its placid waters and unpromising winds, is not an area likely to be troubled, if that is the right word to use. Perhaps we shall all have to learn to be more tolerant and accept environmental changes. After all, a lattice-like tower supporting rotors blurred by movement would be no more obtrusive than the pylons which we already tolerate.

Chapter Eight

WATER-MILL GAZETTEER OF OXFORDSHIRE

I HAVE INCLUDED hardly any dates to suggest when a mill finished work. After maybe half a century even those few mill owners who are still alive are uncertain, and speculation by locals is not reliable—'when the water was lost' and 'when the wheel shaft broke' have been offered as reasons; but the most likely reason would be that falling trade slowly brought work to a halt. A mill working in conjunction with a farm might continue with a bit of 'own use' work until it became more sensible to obtain proper mixes from the specialist provender mills, and one or two dates gathered do suggest that some mills limped along until after World War Two. Misplaced loyalty prompted a few claims to milling recently done when it was obvious that some derangement made that impossible—but I kept my own counsel.

Where storage ponds were used with certainty I have indicated this, but there may have been others which are no longer recognisable through silting or site works of late date. Unless there was some natural configuration of the ground to advantage, then site works would have been needed to improve the run of the mill stream. Remember when looking at mill waterways you may be investigating work done nearly a thousand years ago, or perhaps improvements spread over the 18th and 19th centuries; anything other than an obvious canal feeder may have become contoured into the locale.

To avoid confusion problem sites have been omitted from the county maps so there will be no reference numbers in the gazetteer, while immediate sites in and around Oxford are on a separate map.

You may be fortunate to have a cherised set of the older 1-inch Ordnance maps, fortunate to the extent that the new metric maps omit mill sites no longer deemed important.

Extra information has been obtained from some pre-19th-century mapmakers whose names appear, notably Bryant, Davis, Ogilby, Overton, Plott and Roque.

Nos. 144/5 and 157/8/9 of the old series cover the county; of the new metric series you will need Nos. 151, 163/4/5, and 174/5.

Legend

OCL. Print or photograph in Oxford City Library (Local History Section).
NO. Transferred from Berkshire to the New Oxfordshire.
S. Surveyed/drawn.　　　　SP. Simmons Papers.
o/s. Overshot.　　u/s. Undershot.　　b/s. Breast shot.

Abingdon
-   (139)   SU 480 962. New Cut or Buggs. House conversion with turbine generating electricity.
-   (137)   SU 486 970. Ock Mill, building now commercial.
            SU 493 969. St Helen's, ditto. Wheel and some gear still there in 1981.
            SU 502 970. Abbey Mill, hotel conversion, wheel still in position.

All four were transferred from Berkshire, the first three on the River Ock, the last on the Thames. Cut Mill is outside Abingdon, listed in Sutton Wick, and called New Cut when the Ock was realigned to accommodate the nearby now-abandoned canal. The Abbey site was Saxon and was rebuilt in Norman times. The owners paid £20 p.a. to Abingdon Corporation until 1939, when a lump sum of £550 was paid to settle the matter. All b/s, Abbey (14ft. by 4ft.) surveyed. OCL various.

Adderbury
-   (20)   SP 469 353. Sore Brook. Domestic. Head pond-feeder.

Adderbury Grounds
-   (28)   SP 470 352. Sore Brook. 15ft. by 8ft. b/s, head pond lost, converted to paper and back to corn. All iron mill work with layshaft drive from pit to cross shaft with bevels up to stones, cone clutch drive to hoist.

Adwell
-   (134)   SU 696 997. Haseley Brook. Lost, shown on Davis's map of 1797. Records of 1548, 1591, 1657/8 and 1790 exist.

Albury (Tiddington)
            Site in doubt, mentioned in 1332, possible confusion with windmill.

Alkerton
-   (6)   SP 379 419. Sore Brook. Domestic, ponds lost, there were three pairs of stones.

Alvescot
-   (109)   276 049. Shill Brook. Complete mixed wood and iron gear, but 13ft. by 4ft. b/s wheel gone. Large pond. S. A Peak stone by Corcoran, London, numbered 143. Bakehouse.

Ardington
-   (169)   SU 429 882. NO. Ginge Brook. Complete wood and iron gear and o/s wheel 11ft. by 4ft. Water lost. Craft workshop, so viewable.

Ascott under Wychwood
-   (64)   SP 309 195. Evenlode. Water lost, but gear fairly complete with well-preserved 13ft. by 6ft. clasp-arm b/s wheel. Three pairs stones.

Ashbury
-   (164)   NO. Cole. Upper mill domestic. Lower mill at SU 262 855 workable with rebuilt wood and iron o/s wheel. North Mill 862 255 appears, but no waterways show on the first O.S. map.

Ashford   *See* Wilcote.

Asthall
(88)   SP 290 114. Windrush. Was a good example of 6ft.-diameter b/s water-wheel driving water pump and Armfield turbine generating electricity. Now site only, shown on 1786 map, but not on 1884. OCL.

Aston Tirrold
        NO. Problem site, could have been a windmill.

Balscote
(7)   SP 391 408. Sore. No water, 12ft. by 5ft. o/s iron wheel, and fairly complete wood and iron gear, two sifters.

Bampton
(116)   SP 311 031. Highmoor Brook. Site only, would have been u/s.

Barford St John
(25)   SP 446 331. Swere. Head pond/feeder diverted. Iron 13ft. by 2ft. o/s wheel and lade, fairly complete iron gear and upright shaft, two pairs stones, decayed wire machine, buildings ruinous. S. Now domestic.

Barford St. Michael
(26)   SP 434 328. Swere. Might be workable. Head pond/feeder to o/s iron wheel 10ft. by 5ft., mostly iron gear and upright shaft with layshaft drive complete on one side only, wood stone nuts. Date stones 1717, 1762, RA 1812. S.

Bayswater
(105)   SP 562 080. Small brook-fed ponds, now dry. Substantial buildings, only hoist left. Chimney and engine house remain. Listed as Forest Hill 1278.

Banbury
(10)   Cherwell. Mill identies lost, Grimsbury SP 459 418 was corn, later steam driven. SP 459 408 was tweed and corn with steam auxiliary power.

Basildon
(181)   Thames. Two adjacent mills recorded in 1795 about SU 603 796, shown on Roque's map in 1761, also noted in 1777—was it Cose Mill?

Beard
(108)   SP 397 055. Windrush. Now farm buildings. Two wheels each drove one pair of stones.

Benson
(162)   SU 618 917. Now domestic, lively stream.

Bicester
        Mill/mills ceased in early 17th century, but waterways could still be traced in the 1950s in the Chapel Street area (SP).

Black Bourton
(110)   Shill Brook. Of the two Domesday mills listed an abandoned site at SP 284 044 is likely to have been one, and the other at Mill

Farm SP 294 042 where only the wooden shaft remains of the enclosed 13ft. by 6ft. l/b/s wheel. Mixed wood and iron gear drives two pairs of burrs (no stone furniture) and slack belt hoist lying parallel to ridge. Shown by Davis. The feeder is very long and looks artificial; where it passes closely behind Manor Farm SP 287 039 there is a late-19th-century outside iron l/b/s wheel 9ft. by 6ft. powering a countershaft in the barn to drive farm machinery.

Bladon
(79)   SP 437 146. Evenlode. On Davis's map. There is a record of stones fetched from Banbury in 1246.

Bletchington
(70)   SP 482 182. Cherwell. Enslow Mills. Equipped with modern gear and rollers driven by gas engine when sold in 1928.

Blewbury
(175)   SU 533 873. NO. Mill Brook. Pond and head of water. Domestic. OCL. SU 537 873. Iron b/s wheel of same design as East Hagbourne. Heavy wooden shaft and interesting wooden and iron pit wheel, exposed and will continue to decay.

Bodicote
(19)   SP 458 372. Sore. Domestic. Some gear remains, but no water. OCL.

Botley
          On Oxford map. SP 491 062. Seacourt Stream. Site only. *The story of Botley Mill,* published privately by Charles Broadhurst in 1970. OCL.

Broadwell
(120)   SP 257 026. Broadwell Brook. Galloways Mill. Water lost to wheel, which is iron 8ft. by 8ft. o/s with iron lade, some inside gear remains. S.

Broughton
(12)   SP 408 384. Sore Brook. Ruinous buildings of what was a fulling mill and then paper. Four spoked hub of iron water-wheel remains and various stone-paved waterways. If this was 'Upper fulling mill' (Davis) was 419 381 the lower?

Broughton Pogges
(115)   SP 236 040. Broadwell Brook. Buildings well preserved, including pack-horse stables and toll house. Ponds, now no water. Collapsed 14ft by 4ft. 6in. b/s clasp arm wooden wheel, some metal/wood gear, hoist lies parallel to ridge, burr made up in cast iron frame. S.

Bruerne
          A document of 1713 mentions two water grain mills at Bruerne-Tangley with no hint of location.

Burford
(85)   SP 251 127. Windrush. Town Mills. Present structure built to house wheel-driven pumps for local water supply. Repairable/workable

13ft. by 9ft. u/s compass arm wooden wheel, but no gear. S. 258 120. Windrush. Corn/electricity/laundry, latterly with turbine and at one time with auxiliary steam power, the engine having been bought from Charlbury Brickworks second-hand in 1890. In 1897 there were five sets of rollers and one pair of stones; in this year a fire prevented further milling; in fact, a series of fires have dogged subsequent activities there, and the buildings are now demolished.

Buscot
(130)   NO. Thames. SU 247 986 Eaton Hastings, SU 231 980 Harts Lock, pond-driven turbine at SU 242 973 and SU 250 960, all part of private industrial complex established in 1859, long since bankrupted. *See Industrial Archaeology*, Vol. 8, No. 2.

Cassington
(96)   SP 449 100. Evenlode. A large later 19th-century stone building on four floors, now stripped out. Water good. Worked up to last war with up-dated gear, turbine-driven with auxiliary oil engine.

Castle   On Oxford map. Site only, water good.

Chadlington
(56)   Davis shows two sites around SP 325 220, still recognisable.

Charlbury
(68)   SP 353 198. Evenlode. Had two pair peaks, one pair burrs, stripped and adapted to pump local water supply in 1896.

Chalford
(127)   SP 721 010. Stream-fed large pond, last worked with turbine, which remains. Gear dismantled, but bed stones remain. Recorded 1341, 1542.

Chalgrove
(135)   SU 631 970. Marl Brook. Complete metal gear save crown wheel, two pairs stones, water good, but unlikely to be workable. o/s 11ft. by 6ft. 6in. metal wheel, wooden lade. S.

Challow
(159)   SU 367 894. NO. Childrey Brook. Site only.

Charney Bassett
(143)   SU 382 944. NO. Ock. 14ft. by 7ft. u/s wheel gone, otherwise complete with wood/iron gear, but water poor. There were large ponds and stone-lined sheep-wash. Mill museum here distinctly possible. S.

Chesterton
(61)   SP 564 214. Site only on viable stream, shown by Davis.

Chevaliers
          On Oxford Map.

Chipping Norton
(40)   SP 296 266. Hartleys Mill. Ruins on site and mill stone.

Chiselhampton
          River Thame. Domesday site, long gone.

Cholsey
(177)   SU 602 870. NO. Thames. Roque's map 1761. Domestic.

Churchill
(47)   SP 275 248. Pond dry, sluices remain, all gear stripped from sub-
          stantial building.

Church Enstone
(49)   SP 277 348. Tributary Glyme. 11ft. by 4ft. o/s metal wheel, lade,
          and gear complete, but only one pair stones remain. Might be
          worked with overhaul. Head pond/feeder. Bread oven. S.

Cleeve
(179)   SU 601 815. Thames. Now domestic, formerly two wheels, of which
          one now remains to generate electricity for domestic use. Outside
          bearing support to wheel as Mapledurham and Crowmarsh. OCL.

Clevely
(53)   Two adjacent mills around SP 388 240. Glyme with large ponds,
          probably o/s. Upper now domestic, lower farm buildings with
          some dismantled gear and stones remaining. S. Refit by Lampitts
          in 1883 with three pairs stones. Date stone WT 1789. One
          unidentified was fulling mill in 1643. A burr by Hughes & Sons,
          London. Wire machine.

Clifton
(30)   SP 492 319. Cherwell. A larger mill which had two metal b/s wheels.
          One set fairly complete metal/wood gear remains, and 14ft. by
          4ft. 6in wheel (3ft. 6in. gone). Might be workable. Grain elevator
          and storage for over 600 bushels. Fail safe on sack hoist. S.

Cokethorpe
(103)   SP 374 066. Windrush. Corn mill adapted to pump estate water in
          form of Gothic tower and known as 'The Fish House'. Recent

domestic conversion—there was a well-preserved 9ft. by 4ft. oak u/s compass arm wheel inside building. Date stone 27 IA 23 with 'repard' (repaired?) OCL. S.

Coleshill
(141) SU 234 935. NO. Cole. Water looks good, might be worked. Estate generator and pump, fairly complete iron gear. 11ft. by 5ft. 6in. metal b/s wheel by Phillips of Reading. N.T. property.

Combe
(78) SP 417 150. Evenlode. Domesday site adapted to large saw-mill for Blenheim Estate in 1850s. Water lost to 13ft. by 8ft. metal b/s wheel. Auxiliary beam engine restored and steamed as part of countryside museum. S.

Cornwell
Possibly SP 276 269. May have disappeared when bridge replaced ford. Mill Copse nearby.

Cothill
(131) SU 466 997. NO. (Dry Sandford.) Domestic. Old lease shows this as o/s with large ponds, now dry.

Cowley
On Oxford map.

Crawley
(91) *See* Witney.

Croperdy
(2) SP 470 458. Cherwell. Later brick building remains, but no access achieved. British waterways.

Crowmarsh
(167) SU 614 911. Thames. When house conversion was done some fine decorative date stones were preserved. Two metal b/s wheels remain (17ft. by 9ft. 6in., and 16ft. by 8ft.). Long vulnerable life, by 1866 it was busy with corn and bone grinding; in 1910 it was a flock mill; and in 1922 it generated electricity for the area. Both wheels have the (peculiar?) Thames adjustable outside bearings. OCL. S.

Cuddesdon
(123) SP 612 028. Thame. Stripped outbuildings remain, lively water under. SP 595 045. Cuddesdon Brook. A lost early site, a second mill recorded in area of lost village of Combe.

Culham
    NO. Possible site at around SU 506 946.

Cut
(112)   SP 405 042. Windrush, now farm buildings.

Cutt
(140)   SU 662 962. Tributary Marl Brook, with large pond now lost. 12ft by 8ft. metal o/s wheel fed by metal lade. Fairly complete lower gear, with metal elevators from three pairs of stones up to bins. Domestic.

Cuttle
(50)   *See* Lower Heyford.

Cuxham
(146)   SU 672 952. Marl Brook. Domestic, with 12ft. by 6ft. metal b/s wheel retained within. Feeder and pond lost.

Dean
(57)   SP 344 221. Two streams were channelled round hillside to feeder pond, thence by pipe to box and metal lade to 12ft. by 4ft. o/s metal wheel. Water lost. Domestic, retaining most of wood/metal gear in house. S.

Deddington
(27)   SP 455 329. Swere. Stripped. Retained sluice gear bears Gilkes name, the mill last worked on a turbine.

Drayton
(152)   SU 490 935. NO. Mill Brook, which starts as Ginge Brook. Largish stone-grinding mill with haphazard collection of up-dated cleaning and sifting gear, driven by dished b/s metal wheel. Bradfields Mill. Some parts recently burned out, other parts used as engineering shop.

Dry Sandford
    See Cothill.

Ducklington
(100)   There were two mills on the Windrush, possibly both corn/cum fulling. Sp 358 081 has gone (marked Tucking Mill 1823). SP 361 073 has been modernised for animal feeds; it had lay shaft drive to the stones and steam auxiliary power. Flax processing in 1850s. Which of them was Kill Mill (1715) and Knipes Mill (1850)?

East Hagbourne

(171)   SU 539 875. NO. Ginge Brook. A complete mill with metal/wood gear and good water which might be worked. Survey by J. K. Major. SU 542 878. A paper mill downstream, marked as ruinous in 1860.

East Hanney

(151)   SU 416 932. NO. Letcombe Brook. A late 19th-century building stripped out.

East Hendred

(166)   A fairly complete mill at SU 454 890 (NO) is used as a craft shop, and a wood and tile building, at 456 896, is stripped out (Ludbridge Mill), both on Ginge Brook.

Enstone

See Church Enstone.

Epwell

(8)   SP 360 403. Sore. Domestic.

Ewelme

(163)   SU 638 919. The site of a wooden mill destroyed by fire in 1886 is marked by a change in level in the watercress beds.

Eynsham

(93)   SP 438 108. Evenlode. A corn mill which became a noted paper mill; only mill house remains.

Fawler

(71)   SP 369 172. Evenlode. Site only.

Filkins

(118)   241 036. Broadwell Brook. Domestic. Head pond/feeder; wheel chamber remains and some stones on site.

Forest Hill

See Bayswater.

Friars Farm

(156)   222 905. NO. Cole. Farm buildings.

Fringford

(37)   SP 613 287. Tributary Ouse. Fairly complete gear, b/s 12ft. by 5ft. wooden compass arm wheel, which had auxiliary steam. Refurbished for milling 1978. S.

Fullwell
(22)   SP 626 349. Great Ouse. Site Only. Once held by Osney Abbey.

Gaunt
(119)   SP 405 030. Windrush. Domestic, with water running under. Some hursting timber retained.

Gill
(104)   SP 380 070. Windrush. Now farm buildings.

Ginge
        SU 445 872. NO. Ginge Brook; shown disused in 1860.

Glympton
        Glyme. Possibly the mill referred to in 18th-century Kiddington estate records.

Godington
(39)   Site only on tributary Ouse about SP 650 283.

Goosey
        Area SU 360 920. NO. Problem site with nearby references to Millway and Millway Farm.

Goring
(180)   SU 596 807. NO. Thames. A large wooden mill now used as a commercial building, with water passing under. OCL.

Great Bourton
(3)   SP 472 450. Cherwell. Now Peewit Farm.

Great Milton
        Four mills recorded in the parish in the 16th century, possibly on the Marl Brook one east of Ascot Farm noted in 15th century.

Great Rollright
(33)   SP 303 297. Can still be traced on site.

Great Tew
(34)   Traces of pond, canal and wheel chamber at SP 395 299, the site of mill built for wool processing in 17th century. Traces of ponds and buildings, with two water-wheels at SP 402 304, still referred to locally as 'bone mill'.

Grove
(160)   SU 400 896. NO. Possibly restoration, with existing 'Rivers' turbine driving small mill by belt. Was known as Cane Mill.

Hampton Gay

(73) SP 485 166. Cherwell. Corn to paper in 17th century. Ruins and waterways remain, some gear in head water and part of b/s metal wheel in chamber.

Hampton Poyle

(77) SP 498 154. Cherwell. Site only. Davis showed this mill, but omitted nearby Kidlington.

Hardwick

(107) SP 380 061. Windrush. Some lay-shaft gear remains, but 12ft. by 5ft. u/s wheel has gone. Wheel chamber paved with gravestones. Had steam auxiliary with belt drive to extended l/h layshaft. S.

Hardwick

North of Banbury on Cherwell. Maybe confused with nearby Huscot, but no records after 1915. Mill Field recorded to s/w in 1279 may have marked windmill site.

Hazelford

(11) SP 405 390. Tributary. Sore. Corn mill became paper mill; now site only.

Headington

Kings Mill on Oxford map; Headington parish.

Henley

(182) SU 775 816. Thames. Last worked as paper mill.

Henton

N/E of Chinnor. Recorded in 1289, gone by 1468.

Holywell

On Oxford map. A Melchair print of 1770 shows a four-square large building. OCL.

Holton

(113) SP 613 058. Thame. 11ft. by 7ft. 6in. b/s metal wheel and fairly complete wood/metal gear. Water active. Unique sack trolley and turntable on catwalk to storage bins. OCL. S.

Hook Norton

The two Domesday mills listed have been lost in obscurity, though Swerford Mill is often confused. *The English Register of Osney Abbey* (1913 Clarke) mentions a third mill in 1260 fed by Kerswell Lake in the East Field.

Hordley
(69)   SP 444 189. Glyme. Traces on site. Mill Ford upstream is misleading,
        being a corruption of Milk Ford, but there was a small wheel-
        driven pump a bit above that.

Horley
(4)   SP 418 436. Tributary Sore. Traces on site, ceased 1920. Site only
        at 423 432.

Horton cum Studley
        SP 602 126. Stream presently culverted, once fed pond (now depres-
        sion) at Wier Cottage.

Huscote
(5)   SP 469 426. Cherwell. Site marked by modern water control sluice.

Iffley
(122)   SP 526 037. Thames. Wheel b/s. Mill destroyed by fire in 1908.
        OCL.

Ilbury
        Area SP 435 305. A mill recorded in 17th century variously named
        Nether Worton, Worton, or Ilbury. Davis does not show it.

Islip
(84)   SP 520 137. Cherwell. House only remains, mill buildings straddling
        water demolished 1945. A large mill, but never modernised, last
        worked with 17ft. and 15ft. metal wheels, both u/s.

Kidlington
(83)   SP 502 140. Cherwell. A large mill, never modernised. Two metal
        b/s wheels approximately 13ft. by 4ft. remain, and most of both
        sets of wood/metal gear. S.

Kingham
(55)   SP 259 233. Tributary Evenlode. Now hotel, o/s wooden wheel
        retained.

Kings Mill
        See Headington.

Kingston Blount
        Early records may be confused with nearby Chalford, *which see*.

Kirtlington
(66)   SP 487 195. Cherwell. A large mill with only one 13ft. by 5ft. b/s

wood/metal wheel now driving generator for restored domestic use, never modernised as mill. Flights Mill. Stones on site. S.

Langley
(67)   SP 292 181. Evenlode. Only shaft remains to u/s wheel, with complete three pairs stone gear.

Launton

Canon J. Blomfield, writing of this area a century ago, mentioned a water-mill ('a winter mill') in area SP 601 232, supplanted by a windmill nearby in 1275. Field names record the sites, now lost through development. (Bodleian Library MS. D.D. Par. Launton b6.)

Letcombe Bassett
(174)   SU 377 856. NO. Letcombe Brook. Was a fulling mill, house on site, water lively through water-cress beds.

Letcombe Regis
(168)   SU 382 870. NO. Letcombe Brook. Domestic. A fulling/corn mill is still shown on the first O.S. map at 387 873.

Lewknor

About SU 711 981. Possibly Nethercote. Records suggest it was superceded by a windmill in 16th century.

Lidstone
(48)   SP 358 248. Glyme. Long head pond/feeder. Dismantled a few years ago, leaving a 24ft. by 4ft. metal o/s wheel fed through pipe to box and flume and a 15ft-pit wheel. Wood/metal gear drove three pairs stones, and the bread oven was part of an active baker's trade. A large mill. S.

Little Clanfield
(125)   157 270. Broadwell Brook. Overton labels it Blagraves Mill. 14ft. by 2ft. b/s metal wheel worked till 1940, powering a straw-rope factory. Now domestic; wheel remains. S.

Little Faringdon
(128)   223 011. Leach. 14ft. by 6ft. 6in. metal b/s wheel drove layshaft to horizontal shaft up to three pairs of stones through bevels. Beautifully made late 19th-century mill work. This mill continued to work later than most, possibly till 1970. An 8ft. o/s metal wheel pumped the local farm water.

Long Handborough
(82)   SP 438 138. Evenlode. Buildings stripped out. Last worked with two wheels and five pairs stones. 12in. thick peaks on site.

Lower Grove
(29)   SP 463 369. Sore. Domestic.

Lower Heyford
(51)   SP 489 250. Cherwell. Some metal gear left (no wheel), the spur cast as a flattened cone (as Radford) to bring the rim in the same plane as the wallower. SP 481 251. Tributary Cherwell. Cuttle Mill. Domestic. Faced to simulate a rustic cottage by Wm. Kent in 1740 for Rousham Estate. 'Temple of the mill.'

Lower Tadmarton
(16)   SP 403 372. Sore. Domestic. Stripped save for hoist.

Mapledurham
(185)   SU 669 769. Thames. Wooden b/s wheel carried on adjustable outside bearing recently restored (Cleeve, Crowmarsh). A second wheel at the opposite end of the mill had been replaced by a turbine to generate and pump for estate. In 1791 there were three wheels and choice of powering a tilt hammer, a metal rolling mill, or any one of six pairs of stones. OCL.

Marcham
(138)   SU 458 953. NO. Ock. Worgen Mill in 18th century. Domestic. Wheel shaft on site. OCL.

Merton Grounds
        Around SP 580 190. Ray. 'A mill set up by the Templars on the East Brook' in 1150. I have a map of 1900 showing a mill at SP 578 203 of which there is no other record.

Middle Barton
(45)   SP 439 257. Dorn. Domestic. OCL.

Middle Mill
(147)   SU 673 952. Marl Brook. Large dry pond. Domestic.

Milcombe
        Was probably South Newington.

Milton
(157)   SU 480 926. NO. Ginge Brook. Site only.

Milton under Wychwood
(62)   273 181. House on site. Worked from pond fed by small stream. 'Mill Hill' appears two miles S/W at SP 228 164.

Minster Lovell

(90)   SP 317 112. Windrush. Building restored, no millwork. There were two wheels driving four pairs of stones.

Mixbury

See Fullwell. Two early mills around SP 612 347. Willaston mentioned in records, also Upper and Nether Mill Fields (windmill?).

Mollington

Water-mill first noted 13th century. All traces lost.

Mongewell

(176)   SU 610 878. Worked from large pond, Carmel College now occupies the site.

Monks

SP 323 001. Thames. Shown by Roque in 1761 at Rushey Weir.

Moor (Baulking)

See Uffington. SU 308 908. NO. Domestic.

Morrells Brewery

On Oxford map. *See* chapter on Applied Power. 13ft. by 3ft. 6in. metal b/s wheel, wood starts/paddles. S.

Newbridge

(121)   SP 402 019. Last mill on Windrush. Domestic.

New Cut

(139)   SU 480 962. NO. Ock. Buggs Mill, renamed when river was realigned to accommodate nearby canal. Domestic, turbine generates electricity.

New

See Witney.

North Aston

(36)   SP 493 291. Cherwell. Often confused with Somerton. Water flows under house conversion; stones on site.

North Brook

(58)   SP 488 222. Cherwell. Catsham Mill in 1844. Site only, line of mill-stream shown on Tithe Map.

North Newington

(13)   SP 424 394. Sore. Collesmill in 1444. Corn, converted to paper in 1684, then bone-grinding, and back to corn in World War I

with belt-driven single pair stone free-standing mill. 18ft. by 7ft. b/s metal wheel still workable from right-angled iron penstock. 15ft. pitwheel remains, some artifacts on site, and ventilated paper-drying shed.

North Stoke
(178)   SU 611 863. Domestic. Stream water active under house. Turbine still in place.

Nuneham Courtenay
(132)   Around SU 539 998. Thames. On Domesday List, recorded again in 1279; long gone.

Old Chalford
(43)   SP 343 257. Glyme. Corn mill site rebuilt as bone mill, 12ft. 6in. by 5ft. o/s metal wheel fed from large pond. Pitwheel drove layshaft then by belt up to 125ft.-long shafting into base of bone mill sited higher up bank. S.

Overy
(154)   SU 583 941. Thame. 15th-century wooden mill, large, but never modernised. Both u/s wheels have gone, but some iron gear remaining; also wooden pit and wallower. OCL. S.

Osney
        On Oxford map. SP 498 059. Thames. Associated with 12th-century Osney Abbey. Rebuilt in present form in 1845 as large brick mill on 4½ floors, with turbine and steam auxiliary driving four pairs of burrs, saw-mill and bone-mill. Destroyed by fire in 1946. Some gear remains within ruins; and turbine. OCL.

Over Norton
        See Priory.

Peewit
        See Great Bourton.

Piddington
        About SP 640 170 in 1270.

Pinkhill
(101)   SP 443 075. Thames. John Roque 1761 and Davis 1793. Site only.

Priory
(31)   SP 333 299. Top mill on Swere with large storage pond, now domestic. Stones on site.

Pusey

NO. Possibly in area SU 375 965.

Queenford
(145) SU 585 950. Thame. Buildings stripped, bins and hoist (controlled directly on sack floor) remain.

Radcot
(129) SU 285 995. NO. Thames. The bridge was a key point of fierce fighting in the 12th, 14th, and 17th centuries, when no doubt the adjacent mill would have suffered. There are records of successive mill sites and waterways just above the bridge.

Radford
(54) SP 409 237. Glyme. Most wood/metal gear remains with dished spur in same plane as wallower (*c.f.* Lower Heyford). 11ft. 6in. by 7ft. 6in. o/s metal/wood wheel with wooden lade and tail race in tunnel. Baking oven. S. Possible fulling mill site at SP 407 242.

Salford
(35) SP 292 276. Tributary Evenlode. All metal gear installed in old hursting with three pairs stones. Auxiliary steam drove stone spindles through bevels. Metal lade from pond (now dry) fed 13ft. 6in. by 5ft. o/s metal wheel bearing Lampitt's name. Recently partly stripped, but gear secured. Omitted on Davis's map. S.

Sandford
(126) SP 531 012. Thames. Corn mill of long history converted to paper, with which it continues. Turbines (*see* chapter on Applied Power). OCL.

Sandford St Martin
(44) SP 419 264. Tributary Dorn. Domestic.

Sarsden
(52) SP 288 235. Two 8ft. by 1ft. o/s metal wheels in tandem driving estate water pumps. SP 285 236. Possible site.

Seacourt

NO. Seacourt Stream. Two mills on Domesday List around SP 485 075.

Sescut (Southcourt, Southcote)
(98) SP 524 104. Cherwell. Mill Lane, Old Marston, once led directly to it. Traces of weir remained in 1910, but dredging in two wars

to keep Otmoor drained has left only farm buildings to mark site. Shown by Davis.

Shenington

Possibly confused with Alkerton, and further confusion over possible second site.

Shillingford

SU 594 923. Thames. No trace, 'in ruins' in 1438.

Shiplake

(186)   SU 771 787. Thames. Corn mill converted to paper. Site only. OCL. and various prints.

Shipton under Wychwood

(63)   SP 283 187. Evenlode. Was wheel-driven with steam auxiliary, now a modern provender mill.

Shirburn

Near Watlington. Relative documents of 1151/63.

Sibford Ferris

(14)   SP 345 363. Top mill on Stour. Two mills almost in tandem, lower one stripped, some gear in upper (both probably o/s). Many stones on site including blackstones.

Signet

SP 246 104. b/s wheel 9ft. by 18in. driving two pumps.

Somerton

(42)   SP 490 278. Cherwell. A largish mill using auxiliary steam with some roller gear in 1890, now site only.

Souldern

(32)   SP 511 318. Ockley Brook. Largish mill with stream-fed pond, now dry. Domestic. Once used as silk mill.

South Hinksey

On Oxford City map. SP 519 039. Thames. SP 522 043 Seacourt Stream. Formerly in Berkshire, both corn mills were converted to paper-making and worked till the 1920s; site traces of second; first lies under new road. OCL.

South Moreton

(172)   SU 560 880. NO. Ruinous buildings only.

South Newington
(24)   SP 411 335. Swere. Abandoned buildings on site. SP 406 334. Domestic.

South Weston
(136)   SU 703 983. 17ft. by 4ft. o/s metal wheel fed through metal lade no longer connected to large pond, tail race in tunnel. Fairly complete metal gear, but buildings ruinous. Had auxiliary steam driving in through a second (lower) bevel spur. S.

Spelbury
(59)   SP 344 211. Tributary Evenlode. Colderne and Coldrun Mill in 17th century. Mill work taken for display in Science Museum and destroyed by enemy action in World War II.

Stadhampton
(133)   SU 604 985. Marl Brook. Large pond now dry. 9ft. by 5ft. o/s metal wheel and well preserved wood/metal gear. S.

Standlake
(117)   SP 397 039. Windrush. 11ft. by 5ft. b/s metal wheel and one side of wood/metal layshaft gear remains. Hurst forms mezzanine floor. Bread oven. Overton shows it as Shuffords Mill. SP 400 034. Abandoned fulling mill site.

Stanford in the Vale
(142)   SU 342 940. Tributary Ock. NO. Domestic. SU 344 927. Tributary Ock. Stones and part of metal wheel on site. Domestic.

Stanton St John
(99)   Wheel chamber and large dry ponds once fed by streams exist.

Steeple Barton
        See Sandford St Martin.

Steventon
(161)   SU 465 914. NO. Ginge Brook. Domestic.

Stratton Audley
(38)   SP 627 285. Tributary Ouse. Domestic. Had steam auxiliary. Burrs on site and wheel shaft indicating 4ft.-wide b/s.

Sutton Courtenay
(153)   SU 498 934. NO. Ginge Brook. Laceys Mill. Complete wood/metal gear with workable b/s metal wheel driving two pairs stones and and saw. SU 498 938. Domestic. No trace of water supply.

SU 504 945. Ruins of corn/paper mill. Thames. SU 510 948. Possible site (Culham?).

Swalecliffe
(15)   SP 385 386. Sore Brook. Burned-out buildings. The o/s wheel drove a layshaft through rim gearing (SP).

Swerford
(23)   SP 375 313. Swere. Domestic. Confused with Hook Norton.

Swinbrook
(87)   SP 283 119. Windrush. Water active, but wheel gone (b/s). Domestic. Fairly complete wood/metal gear. OCL. Two pairs stones.

Sydenham
(124)   SP 728 016. Large ponds from stream, had steam auxiliary, then oil engine. Fine hursting retained. Tail race in tunnel.

Tackley
(60)   SP 484 204. Cherwell. Pulback Mill. Moor Mill on records of 1621 at Nethercot—is this a second mill?

Taston
        SP 361 218. Tributary Evenlode. Wheel-driven water pump for drinking fountain in 1862.

Taynton
(80)   236 132. Windrush. Complete wood/metal gear and two pairs stones recently removed for conservation elsewhere. 12ft. by 3ft. b/s wheel gone, but retained hub indicates 12 spokes and internal bracing rods, on roller bearings. Paddles from previous wheel used as piling to support bank at abandoned sluice. S.

Thame
(106)   SP 706 068. Thame. Modern laundry on site.

Thrupp
(76)   SP 483 159. Cherwell. Mill ceased owing to canal works in 1793 when company bought the mill from Kidlington Parish. Buildings not recognisable, but tail race traceable.

Tiddington
        Pond at SP 655 048. Albury Mill recorded in 1332, which might have been windmill. A mill stone was found in the area in 1910.

Town
(94)   *See* Witney.

Traceys Farm

(41)   SP 398 268. Purbridge Brook/ponds. 16ft. by 4ft. metal/wood b/s wheel with rim gear fed by metal lade, tail race in tunnel. *See* chapter on Applied Power. Ironwork by Eagle Furnace Co.

Uffington

(149)   SU 300 892. NO. Tributary Ock. Domestic. Two sites. *See* Moor Mill.

Underdown

(111)   SP 373 067. Windrush. Decayed wheel shaft and some gear in ruinous building. One pair peaks, one pair Dell's burrs; had wire machine.

Upper Grove

(18)   SP 452 371. Sore. Second-hand turbine installed in 1856, failed 1900. Domestic.

Upper Heyford

(46)   SP 492 262. Cherwell. (Heyford Warren). Site only, was u/s. Photo in Underhill album.

Upton

(81)   240 127. Windrush. Site only. Corn to paper, back to corn 1835.

Venn

(144)   SU 396 880. Childrey Brook. NO. Benn Mill on 1793 map. Metal gear and b/s wheel complete, restoration proceeding.

Wallingford

(173)   NO. Despite its long foundation and proximity to the river mill evidence is scrappy. In 1300 there were four mills near the Castle and one other nearby. In 1528 Henry VIII granted the lease of two mills near the Castle. At this time Pollington's Weir was built across the main river and a mill stream down through the Castle area fed two corn and two fulling mills. The weir was a nuisance to river traffic and was removed in 1790. The Boughton family appear in later years as millers, and one who says he worked at the mill (608 891) suggests that some water power was still in use in 1965.

Wantage

(165)   SU 396 880. NO. Letcombe Brook. A modernised working mill of long history. SU 395 879. Domestic. Ham Mill 390 373 retains a 17ft. 6in. by 4ft. 6in. metal wheel on metal shaft by Gibbons of Wantage, some gear *in situ* and burr on site. Recent excavations have revealed a decayed 11ft. by 6ft. metal wheel on wooden

shaft by Guttridge, Wallingford, fed o/s from ornamental lake which fed the other wheel at 10 o'clock b/s, or this wheel could be fed 5 o'clock b/s from a stream pond.

Wardington
(1)   SP 488 476. Cherwell. Domestic. A wind/cum water-mill, some gear retained on site.

Watchfield
(148)   231 909. NO. Cole. Privately preserved as mill museum. 11ft. by 2ft. 8in. b/s metal wheel has only one set of spokes.

Waterstock
(114)   SP 633 056. Thame. Domestic.

Watlington
(155)   SU 678 950. Marl Brook and ponds. Domestic.

West Ginge
        SU 445 873. NO. Ginge Brook. Last worked as paper mill.

West Hanney
(150)   SU 413 927. Letcombe Brook. Large premises with all gear stripped out, last worked on turbine.

West Hendred
(170)   SU 453 887. NO. Ginge Brook. Domestic.

Weston on the Green
(74)   SP 529 186. Gallos Brook and pond. No gear. Domestic. There is a mysterious Bryan Donkin water-gate control buried between pond and wheel, but no record of a turbine.

Whitchurch
(183)   SU 635 769. Thame. A large mill, last used to generate local electricity by two metal b/s wheels on same shaft. Domestic. OCL.

Widford
(86)   273 118. Windrush. Substantial buildings stripped for farm use One-time paper mill worked from large pond. Davis shows two mills in tandem. *See* chapter on Applied Power.

Weirs
        See South Hinksey.

Wiggington
(23)   SP 391 330. Swere. Domestic.

Wilcote
(75)   SP 385 156. Evenlode. Stripped buildings.

Witney

Windrush. Woodford, Worsham (89), New (92), Town (94), and Crawley (91) were all corn mills adapted and engaged as the wool industry demanded. Possibly all had auxiliary power; there was certainly steam at New and a turbine at Worsham. Farm Mill (95) at SP 360 092 remained a corn mill, but was at one time manufacturing fertiliser (bone?) with steam auxiliary power. The mill attached to Cogges Priory was around SP 361 097, and was probably one of the Witney mills included in the Domesday list.

Wolvercote
(97)   SP 487 098. Thames. An early corn mill which became a paper mill and has continued so, *see* chapter on Applied Power. There are some early references to a mill at Godstow Nunnery. If there was a site later river works will have removed all traces; or perhaps we should look to nearby Wolvercote.

Woodstock
(72)   SP 442 169. Glyme. Two 14ft. diameter metal b/s wheels, now dismantled, powered a corn mill and water pumps, *see* chapter on Applied Power. S. Parch marks appearing during a recent drought revealed the ground plan of a mill and pond at SP 439 170 which must have been stream and pond powered, and abandoned when the lake was created in 1760.

Woolstone
(158)   SU 295 882. NO. Site only.

Wooton (Oxon)
(65)   SP 440 196. Glyme. Head pond feeder with steam auxiliary. Domestic with hursting retained. The road forded the tail race before the present bridge was built.

Worsham
(89)   *See* Witney.

Wroxton
(9)   SP 398 405. Sore. Domestic.

Wykham
 (17)   SP 435 375. Sore. Now operating as provender mill with modern
         gear. 15ft. by 8ft. b/s metal wheel remains, but not in use, with
         head pond and feeder.

Wytham
 (102)   SP 477 091. NO. Seacourt Stream. Domestic. Underhill photograph.

Chapter Nine

WINDMILL GAZETTEER OF OXFORDSHIRE

It is not possible to locate some sites accurately enough to provide a grid reference

Adderbury

Ogilby shows a windmill on either side of the road to the west of Nell Bridge (SP 495 343) in the 17th-century. Overton shows only one in 1715.

Adwell

See South Weston.

Albury (Tiddington)

There are records of Windmill Hill and Windmill Field. Humphries, the Thame millwright, collected a mysterious mill-stone from this area in 1920.

Alkerton

A mill shown on Overton's map.

Ambrosden

A mill recorded here in 1300. Windmill Field and Millway appear.

Arncott

SP 614 172. A typical post mill (one pair of stones in breast, one pair in tail) stood in decay in 1945, and there are some remains on the site, which is private. Last worked with common sails. A suggestion that this mill was brought from Bicester in 1849 (SP).

Baldon (Toot)

A mill stood in Catsbrayn Field, and there are records of Millway Green and Millhill Field.

Bampton

Windmill House at SP 314 039, but no record of a mill.

Banbury

SP 457 398. Post mill at Easington on the east side of the Oxford road, demolished in the early 18th century. Both Overton and Ogilby show it and there is a small print in *Victoria County History*. SP 441 391. A post mill on the Broughton Road noted by Ogilby. Demolished in 1823 and its duties taken on by nearby Berry Moor Mill which had been built about 1820, further documented in 1832.

Beckley
Approximately SP 566 106. There are 13th-century references to the Lord's Mill, Mill field, recorded, and 17th-century references to a second mill belonging to the vicar.

Begbroke
Davis marks a Windmill Hill between Yarnton and Begbroke which appears as Spring Hill on later maps.

Bicester
SP 584 236 to the east of Buckingham Road and SP 565 225 on the Middleton road, blown down in 1881. One site dates back to 1285. Overton and Ogilby marked them, and there is a print in OCL.

Blackthorn
SP 612 205. There are the remains of two tower mills in this area. The west is now truncated; the tower was plastered and it had a fantail. The east mill still stands to curb level; it was tile-hung and had endless chain weathering.

Bloxham
Overton shows a mill to the west, not well defined.

Bloxham Grove
SP 456 367. A small post mill built 1865. Well maintained until recently. One pair of 30in. stones driven directly from above, with governor. Cloths rolled down sail frames. Surveyed and drawn.

Charlton on Otmoor
SP 567 164. A post mill built possibly 1610; demolished 1905. The tump still exists.

Cropredy
Recorded in 1719, but omitted in the 1742 survey. Wilfred Seaby, the Warwickshire historian, has a record of a mill moved to Avon Dassett in 1725.

Chinnor
SP 750 010. A large post mill working till 1923 with patent sails and low level fantail. Dismantled in 1967 and the main framing taken out of the county. One of the few mills with a six-way support to post. Had auxiliary steam power. Surveyed and drawn. Mill recorded at Wain Hill and Henton in 1249.

Chipping Norton
Approximately SP 318 272. A post mill which stood through the 19th century. Prints exist.

Clanfield
SP 283 019. A tower mill, ruinous in 1900. Mill Farm is a reminder of the site.

Deddington
SP 456 318 Bryant's map 1823. A 1615 lease mentions three water-mills and one windmill.

Epwell
SP 350 408. Ogilby shows this one. There is a photograph in OCL showing stone tower, patent sails, four-bladed fan, domed cap. Worked till 1912.

Faringdon
SU 293 955. The tump was recently flattened. John Rocque does not show it in 1761, but it appears on a map of 1876. A coloured print in the Shire Hall, Reading, shows a tower mill with domed cap.

Garsington
A mill recorded in 1308.

Goring
Said to be 'by the weir' in 1538.

Great Haseley
SP 638 026. One of the remaining mills with the cap recently replaced and the interior in fair condition. An 1806 date stone on the tower misleads as it was built in 1760. Tower mill, common sails, two pairs stones, friction hoist, two sifters. Had sliding sash windows. 1889 dates ironwork by local foundry and suggests improvements/repairs at that time. Fan tail, surveyed.

Great Milton
SP 617 030. A post mill demolished in 1910, tail pole weathering with cartwheel. Marked Townsend 1820.

Hardwick. Banbury
Mill Field recorded to the south west.

Headington
SP 549 065 and 557 076. One mill was recorded on the first site in 1303, later a second; both were ruinous in the 18th century, and one was rebuilt in 1823. A contemporary folk painting shows a thatched cap

which was not in keeping with local practice. Bryant 1823. The eastern site is probably the post mill shown on a Melchair print of 1771 (OCL) with tail pole and barrel cap; this would be the Windmill Hill on Bryant's map. The mill was painted by William Turner in 1820.

Henley
Some maps show Mill Hill as SU 755 810. Overton shows a mill.

Holton
Davis shows the mill around SP 610 058, which Ogilby did not show a century earlier. Windmill Field is still so named; the base was disturbed during ploughing in 1978.

Hook Norton
SP 365 356 was the site, but no information.

Hornton
SP 389 449. A mill shown on map of 1787 and it had ceased to work in 1869 though it appears on a 1882 map. Stone tower, domed cap, chain weathering gear and common sails.

Iffley
Windmill Close is shown on the Enclosure Map of 1830 to the east of the village.

Ledwell
SP 411 285. Shown by Plott in 1675 and Overton in 1715, but not by Davis in 1793.

Lewknor
There are 16th- to 17th-century records of mills in the area supported by Windmill Field at Postcombe and Windmill Knapp, south of Lewknor.

Little Milton
SP 618 020. A tower mill demolished in 1910. Had shingled cap, endless chain weathering, and common sails. Ochre grinding done.

Little Rollright
A map of 1705 in the County Record Office shows an abandoned site and a new adjacent post mill around SP 291 304.

Merton
Records suggest a mill in this area, but being so near the River Ray it could well have been a water-mill.

Milcombe
A post mill about SP 410 338.

Mixbury

SP 610 346. Upper and Nether Mill Fields recorded; another possible site at Willaston nearby.

Mollington

SP 444 474. A mill noted here in 1545, 1662, 1722, and 1756. The 1797 Enclosure Map shows Mill Quarter, Mill Close and Windmill Fiel. There is still a Mill Farm.

Nettlebed

SU 702 873. The mill Ogilby marked could not have been the one burned down in 1912 for that was first erected near Watlington and moved to this windier site *c*. 1825. It was a slender octagonal smock mill with fantail, outside frames to the body and latterly one pair commons, one pair patents. Painted white. The mill was offered for sale as part of a local pottery in 1894 as 'of 10 h.p.' and let at £2 p.a.

North Leigh

SP 388 129. A tower mill, getting more ruinous. It was restored to working condition 45 years or so ago. There is an outside wooden screw and hand chain for weathering sheltered by dormer roof, common sails.

Nuneham Courtenay

Windmill Hill appers on some maps to the south of the present village.

Oxford

On a 1660 Terrier Map of Holywell Parish in Merton College Library a post mill is shown at the north-east end of St. Giles. Windmill Inn and Windmill Yard marked the site up to 1900.

Salford

SP 292 276. Shown by Davis, who omitted the water-mill. The remains of a tump exist to the east of the Mill House. Rebuilt early 19th century, dismantled 1878.

Sibford Gower

A mill recorded in the 17th century.

South Newington

Overton shows a mill in 1715 (*see* Milcombe).

South Stoke

An 1818 map shows Windmill Ash Field on the slopes of White Hill.

South Weston

SU 703 990. Built 1676, derelict 1818, rebuilt 1852. It had a rather ugly cap weathered by tail pole and cartwheel, one pair of stones and common sails. A photograph shows the mill patched with sheet iron prior to demolition in 1919. There is a possible site on nearby Kop, a mill which may have been moved to Haddenham in the early 19th century. Ochre ground at one time.

Stanton St John

An Enclosure Award map and also Jeffrey's map of 1766 both show a mill about SP 568 085 on Hawkshill Common.

Stokenchurch

SU 751 966, no longer in Oxon. Ogilby shows a mill in 1675. The last mill, of three cross-tree type, was built in 1736 and was seen working as late as 1925, with one pair each of patents and commons.

Stoke Row

SU 685 840. The *Reading Mercury* offered a windmill to let in 1821 and 1838 (SP). Mill base can still be seen; the mill stones form doorstep to mill cottage.

Stonesfield

SP 391 170. A tower mill, ruinous in 1900. Windmill Farm on site. Underhill photograph.

Studley

SP 601 127. Recorded in 1339 and later in 1823 (Bryant); still traces of a tump.

Sydenham

Davis shows a mill about SP 735 035, also Overton. *See* chapter on Mill Stones. Possibly moved to Stone, Bucks. in 1801 (SP).

Thame

SP 705 053. There is a record of a mill in 1594 and a second one built early in the 17th century. Two appear on maps of 1797 and 1880 and continue till the end of the century. Poor photographs exist showing tower mills, one possibly brick, both four-sailers, but (SP) reports one was an eight-sailer driving three pairs of stones.

Towersey

SP 733 062. At the north end of Windmill Road.

Wantage

Windmill Hill shown on some maps about SU 380 874.

Wardington

SP 488 476. A wind/cum water-mill, still recognisable after conversion to domestic use. A mill was erected on Flax Furlong in 1628, near the top of Williamscott, and was still there in 1829. Overton.

Waterperry

Mill Field is recorded on the south side of the Wheatley-Worminghall road.

Waterstock

635 055. Windmill Ground noted in 1663, Windmill Field in 1676 when Ogilby saw the mill, as did Overton in 1715.

Watlington

See Nettlebed. Firest erected SU 073 952.

Weston on the Green

SP 530 220. There is a mound on the left just before the airfield and marked on the 1846 Ordnance Survey map as 'Windmill Clump', but there is no other record of a mill. Ogilby passed right by in the 17th century and did not see one.

Wheatley

SP 589 053. An octagonal masonry tower mill built in 1784, replacing a post mill destroyed in 1767. Common sails, hand crank weathering. A corn mill with an ochre grinder outside. Some dates are noted, but there is confusion with a nearby post mill which was burned down *c.* 1876. Both Overton and Ogilby only show one. Bryant is the only map to show both. Undergoing restoration. Surveyed.

Wykham

The site was just north of the existing water-mill at SP 435 375, and was shown by Ogilby. A mill was noted in 1653, 1675, and 1688, but gone by 1746.

Yarnton

See Begbroke.

In the extended area of New Oxfordshire I have found few windmills. The only well-documented mill is Faringdon. Reference in 1630 at Hinton Waldrist probably apply to a water-mill, as do the lane and field names around Goosey. In 1419 there were two windmills and a fulling mill (which surely must have been a water-mill) working at Sutton Courtney; by 1548 there was only one windmill. There were two in 1608, and both were burned down in 1756.

AN ABANDONED MILL

The pounded waters wasted strength
                    is spent over the weirs,
No splashing wheel to urge the train
                    of sculpted wooden gears,
No movement now within the mill—
                    the stones no longer grind,
No humming thrumming busyness,
                    just wastage left behind.

Few tiles are left upon the roof,
                    the boards gap on the floor,
The rains and snows seep deep below,
                    what matters anymore?
Rust dulls the iron, rot cheats the oak,
                    the woodworm powder scatters,
Soft plaster falls from dampened walls,
                    the boulter hangs in tatters.

Each cog now mutely meshed with cog
                    no longer pitter-patter,
No sacks of grain flip-flap on high,
                    no damsel chitter-chatter.
No miller now to thumb the meal
                    and turn the tenter low,
Where once was life, activity,
                    negated waters flow.

No farmer's cart of gristed grain
                    below the load door stands,
No cottar's hoard patiently gleaned
                    to stir the miller's wand.
No mice, no rats, no miller's cats
                    on their predatory rounds.
No whispering chutes, the mill is mute,
                    and only bird song sounds.

A LIST OF MILLERS
(up to the time of the first [fairly reliable] county directories)

1280	The Bampton Hundreds	
	Walter de Asthall	Asthall
	Jordon de Dentone	Black Bourton
	Alex. Miller, Wm. de Collemor, Thos. de Fileking	Broadwell
	Walter de Raggedemoulle	Filkins
	Robert Nell	Brightampton
	Rich. Miller	Broughton
	Robert Miller	Alvescott
	John and Rbt. Miller	Ducklington
	—. Adam	Ducklington new mill
	John Palmer	Cokethorpe (fulling)
	Jn. Simmonds, Jn. de Flexneye	quarter each Standlake
	Ralph de Monner	Crawley
	Roger and Robt. de Molende	Weald
	Adam de Bede and Thos. de Molende	Clanfield
1532	Wm. Dameroy	Spelsbury
	—. White	Souldern
1546	Rbt. Hawkins	Stanford in the Vale
1556	Nicholas Daye	Wolvercote
1557	John Hawkins	Stanford in the Vale
1582	Thos. Blyth	Bodicote and Bloxham
1584	—. Pitts	Iffley
1599	Hy. Fleming	New Woodstock
1601	Wm. Hawkins	Stanford in the Vale
1605	Ed. Busby	Bloxham
1624	Jn. Berrye	Warmington
1630	Jn. Graunton	Hampton Poyle
	Michael Hawkins	Stanford in the Vale
1640	Richard Smith	Whitchurch
1648	Robert Cossons	Cuxham
1654	Timothy Parsons	Wardington
1656	Peter Nash	Watlington
1658	John Bennett	Stanford in the Vale
1660	Simon Hawkins	Nethercote
	Hamlett Harris	Beard (till 1692)
	Thos. Weale	Beard (late of)
	Stephen Harris	Coldrum (Spelsbury)

1661	Richard Flesher	Iffley
1664	Wm. Slaemaker	Clevely
	Wm. Nowne	Sandford
1670	Wm. Montague	Goring
1671	Richard Grantham	Bicester
	John Gibbs	Chesterton
1672	Thomas Stoakes	Pangbourne
1679	John Bennett	Stanford in the Vale
1682	Wm. Clarke	Goring
1684	Wm. Hall	Bletchington
	John Wade	Islip
1685	Thos. Hawes	Handborough
1688	Wm. Johnson	Ditchley (?)
	John Gibbs	Chesterton
1691	Richard Price	Stanton St John
1692	late held by Jas Marshall, now by Caesar Harris	Burford Town
1698	Wm. Jordan	North Leigh (till 1712)
1705	John Parker	Lower Heyford
	Richard Hollyman	Adwell
1707	Wm. Simmonds	Abingdon
1711	Richard Temple	Thame
	John Harris	Asthall
1712	Jeremiah Beesley	Burford
1716	Richard Hase	Handborough
1717	Richard Faulkner	Warmington
1718	Thomas Matthews	Epwell (till 1747)
1727	Geoffrey Cripps	Thame
1728	William Harris	Beard (till 1763)
1730	John Pates	Chesterton (till 1743)
1732	Timothy Antrum	Whitchurch
1733	Edward Waters	Dorchester
	Edward North	Overy
1734	Wm. Billinghurst	Sonning
	Richard Hartley	Enstone
1741	John Matthews	Wiggington
	Timothy Taylor	Botley
1742	Geoffrey Cripps	Burcot
1743	Jeffrey Cripps the younger	Burcot
1746	Wm. Webb	Cuddesdon
1750	Jn. Batton	Ewelme (also 1761)
1753	A document records five mills: Rd. Goddard, John Clarke, Wm. Cubbidge. Later became two mills: —. Pearman, —. Benwell	Deddington
1753	John Matthews	Epwell (till 1784)

1756	Thos. Lambert	Mollington
1760	Thos. Andrews	Churchill
1761	Edward Bradfield	Milton
1763	Nathaniel Beesley	Burford (till 1794)
1766	John Gardner (deceased)	Bloxham
1773	John Toby	Goring, died 1782
1774	Wm. Moss	Fringford
1780	Thomas Kimber	Burford Port (Town)
	Wm. Brooks	Sandford
1783	John Matthews	Epwell
1786	John Hudson	Combe (till 1800)
1789	James Enser	Kirtlington
1790	Ed. Harris	Standlake
	Thos. Whitley	Standlake
1791	Thos. Whitley	Sandford
1794	Richard Dix	
	Nathaniel Beeseley	Burford
1795	Charles Kimber	Burford
1799	George Ridge	Cholsey
1800	John Coleman	Hordley
1802	Thomas Snowden	Epwell
1806	Nathaniel Sheen	Queenford
1809	Elisha Brownjohn	Mapledurham
1812	John Danbe	Iffley
1813	Thos. Galloway	Chadlington
	Robert Maynard	Weston on the Green
	Wm. Swingburn	Beard.
1814	Richard Lines	Bloxham
	Jeffrey Silver	Great Milton
1815	Thomas Huntley	Burford
1817	Thomas Blackman	Garford (Marcham?)
	William Gilkes	Wiggington
	Richard Lamburn	Holton (later at Wheatley)
1818	Samuel Slack	Brighthampton
1819	Wm. Goodrich	Lidstone
	Wm. Young	Watlington
	Charles Pitman	Mongewell
1823	Gunn's *Directory* lists only:	
	Thos. Burrows	St Peters, Oxford
	Richard Nicholls	Holywell, Oxford
	Henry Vaughan	St Thomas, Oxford
	John Boddington, Jn. Shrimpton	Thame
	John Hine	Watlington
	Thomas Tyrrell	Watlington
	W. Wiggins	Watlington
	Richard Johnson	Woodstock

1824	Thomas Bonner	Somerton
1825	Edward King Atkins	Salford
1826	James Baker	Bletchington
	Thomas Hudson	Combe (till 1846)
	Edward Patrick	Cassington
1827	Thomas Horne	Islip
	John Lister	Radford
1828	Ben. Britnell	Chinnor
1829	Wm. Swingburn	Stanton Harcourt (Beard?)
	(went to Underdown 1832-1841)	
1830	Pigott's *Directory* (Oxford City Library) lists 35	
1831	Wm. Hemmings	Standlake
	Wm. Scroggs	Kidlington
1832	John Cooper	Bodicote
1833	Wm. Winterbourne	Banbury
	Wm. Smith	Wooton
1837	Samuel Beale	Epwell (till 1864)
1840	Thomas Wheeler	Bodicote
	Elisha Brownjohn	Mapledurham
1844	Richard Turner	Alvescott
	Pigott's *Directory* lists 40	
1846	Thomas Cross	Kirtlington
1847	Kelly's *Directory* lists 90, but there are many obvious omissions, a condition which applies to the directories which are available from this date onwards	

Some of the engineer/millwrights known to have worked in the county

undated:

	Smith, Dean, Gilbert	Botley
	Bond	Burford
	Lewindon	Benson
	Ivings	Kiddington
	Hart Soden	Cornwell
1790	John Busby	Deddington
	Jos. Penfold	Wallingford
1825	James Lee	Oxford
1830	Chas. Lampitt	Banbury
	John and Wm. Riley	Banbury
	W. Moss	Banbury
1844	Wm. Rogers	Witney
	Thos. Rose and son	Burford

1847	Francis Kimberly	Banbury
	Stephen King	Standlake
1852	Thos. Lardner	Deddington
	Henry Giles	Hailey
	Hickman	Hardwick
	Jas. Walker	Ducklington
	J. Eagle	Standlake
	Walter Hemmings	Standlake
	W. Mountain	Stanton Harcourt
1855	Wheeler	Oxford

GLOSSARY

Backstays	strengthening support between sail bar and stock.
Bar (sailbar)	lateral member of sail frame.
Bed stone	fixed, lower, nether mill stone.
Bell alarm	a warning device in or near the grain hopper.
Bill (mill bill)	a tool for dressing the mill stones.
Bin	container for meal or grain.
Bist	bran-filled sack used as cushion when stone dressing.
Bolter, boulter, boulting machine	a rotary machine for dressing flour for meal.
Bolting cloth	sifting medium in bolter, beaten internally with rotating wooden laths.
Brake	in a windmill, contracts onto the rim of brake wheel.
Brake wheel	the large drive wheel on the windshaft.
Breyer	an adjustable beam supporting the bridge tree.
Bridge tree	a beam to support bearings as required.
Bridging box	an adjustable housing for a foot step bearing.
Buck	the body of a post mill.
Bucket	*see* paddle.
Burr	a hard quartz millstone imported from France.
Cannister box	*see* poll end.
Cap	the movable top to a smock or tower mill.
Cap centring wheels	metal wheels or rollers provided to facilitate turning the cap and/or maintaining it centrally within the curb.
Cap frame	the main foundation timber of a cap.
Centre post	the wooden post supporting a post mill.
Cill	the level at which the water enters the wheel.
Clasp arm	method of construction of a wooden gear wheel.
Cloths	fabric covering for sail frames.
Cogs	wooden drive teeth housed into metal or wooden gear wheels.
Common sail	an open wooden frame to which the sail cloth is secured.
Compass arm	method of construction of a wheel using radial spokes.
Composition stone	brown stone, black stone. A development of artificial mill stones.
Cracking	the fine lines dressed into the lands.
Crook string	a cord to adjust the slope of the shoe.
Cross trees	the main horizontal beams at the base of a post mill.
Crown tree	the main horizontal structural beam supporting the buck.

136

Crown wheel	the bevel gear wheel at the top of the upright shaft in a water-mill.
Dagger point	the shape assumed by a sail cloth not fully set.
Damsel	a device to shake the grain feed shoe.
Dead curb	a track on which the cap of a windmill turns by sliding, *see* live or shot curb.
Dressing meal	the action of separating the several constituents of the meal.
Dressing stones	preparing the grinding surface of a mill stone.
Dust floor	provided to seal off the cap of a windmill.
Eye	grain feed hole in the centre of a runner stone.
Fan	fantail, a mechanical device to point windmill sails into the wind automatically.
First reef	*see* dagger point.
Float	*see* paddles.
Flume	an artificial channel to bring water to a water wheel.
Footstep bearing	the bottom bearing in which an upright shaft turns.
French burr	*see* burr.
Full sail	fully extended sail cloths.
Furrows	grooves, cut into the grinding surface of a mill stone to lead the meal outwards.
Gate	a control to regulate the flow of water to a water wheel.
Girts	main horizontal construction frames in a buck.
Governor	a speed-controlling device.
Grain floor	garner floor; *see* sack floor.
Great spur	the gear wheel engaging the stone nuts.
Grist	prepared animal feed.
Gudgeon	a metal spindle with three or four fish tails fitted into the ends of wooden shafts.
Harp	one of nine grinding areas of a mill stone.
Hatch	*see* gate.
Hemlath	long light frame connecting the outer end of the sail bars.
Hopper	a wooden funnel shape to direct the flow of grain.
Horse	a frame on the vat supporting hopper and locating damsel.
Hursting (hurst frame)	heavy built-in timber frame supporting the mill work.
Lade	*see* flume.
Lands	grinding areas on mill stones.
Laths	light timber longitudinals of sail frames.
Layshaft (counter drive)	an intermediate shaft transmitting power.
Leading board	an aerodynamic advantage applied to the leading edge of a sail.
Live curb	rollers are attached to the cap frame for ease of turning.
Mace	a connecting piece between stone spindle and rhynd.

Meal	the product obtained after grinding.
Miller's wand	a wooden 'spring' to tension shoe.
Mill race	waterway bringing water to water wheel.
Mill work	all the main driving gear of a mill.
Neck bearing	the front bearing to the wind shaft.
Paddles	flat or curved areas of metal or wood arranged at the rim of a water wheel.
Paint staff	flat wooden surface used to check mill stones before dressing.
Patent sail	a self-regulating sail made up of a series of small shutters.
Peak stone	(Derbyshire peak) quarried from mill stone grit.
Penstock	*see* flume.
Petticoat	vertical boards attached to the cap of a windmill to protect the curb.
Pick (mill pick)	pointed tool for cutting furrows.
Pintle	*see* gudgeon.
Pit wheel	the large main drive gear wheel on the same shaft as the water wheel.
Poll end	a metal end provided to windshaft to house the stocks.
Post mill	a wooden windmill supported on a post.
Proof staff	an accurate metal surface to check the paint staff.
Quarter bars	angled supports between the centre post and the cross trees.
Raddle	a red substance applied to the paint staff.
Roundhouse	a structure enclosing the support frame of a post mill, providing storage
Runner stone	the upper (moving) mill stone.
Rhynd	a heavy metal bar fixed across the eye of the runner stone.
Sack floor	a special storage area for meal or grain provided in a mill; often the attic floor of a water-mill.
Sack hoist	a mechanical contrivance for hoisting sacks of grain or meal.
Sails	energised by wind pressure to provide power for a windmill.
Sail bar	*see* bar.
Second reef	*see* first reef.
Sheers	side members in the cap frame providing support for weather and tail beam, and sprattle.
Shoe	to convey grain from hopper to eye of stone.
Shot curb	(*see* live and dead curbs) rollers spaced out in a separate ring are introduced between curb and cap frame.
Shroud	the 'rim' of a water-wheel has depth enough to enclose the open ends of the paddles.
Shutters	the adjustable areas making up a patent sail.
Slip cogs	removable cogs creating a gap, so disengaging drive between adjacent gear wheels.

Sluice	an adjustable area to control the level or flow of water.
Smock mill	a wooden tower mill, usually eight-sided.
Sole (boards)	a cylindrical wood or metal lining to the water-wheel, creating a 'floor' to the paddles.
Sprattle	a horizontal cross beam in the cap framing carrying the top bearing of the upright shaft.
Spur wheel	*see* great spur.
Staff	*see* paint staff.
Starts	radial wood or metal supports to the paddles.
Stocks	the heavy timber cross to which the sail frames are secured.
Stone casing	a light wooden case enclosing the mill stones.
Stone floor	the floor of a wind- or water-mill where the mill stones are sited—always the first floor in Oxon.
Stone nut	a small gear on the stone spindle driven by the spur.
Stone spindle	transmits the drive up to the runner stone.
Swallow	a slight hollow at the inner grinding area of the stones.
Sword point	sail cloth set in narrow pointed shape.
Tail beam	a horizontal cross beam carrying the tail bearing of the wind shaft.
Tail bearing	the rear bearing of the wind shaft.
Tail pole	a long pole used to wind the cap of a windmill.
Tail race	a waterway carrying water from the wheel.
Temse	an early rocking device for sifting meal.
Thrift	a wooden handle with a mill pick or bill wedged into it for stone dressing.
Tower mill	a windmill built of brick or masonry.
Truck wheels	trolley wheels, curb wheels.
Tump	an artificial mound to raise the height of a windmill.
Tun	*see* stone casing.
Upright shaft (centre shaft)	transmits the power in either wind-or water-mill, carrying the wallower, the spur, the crown wheel.
Vat	*see* stone casing.
Wallower	a gear driven by the pit wheel (water-mill) or the brake wheel (windmill).
Weather	the twist built into windmill sails.
Weather, to	the action of turning the sails into the wind.
Weather beam	the heavy timber beam supporting the neck bearing of the wind shaft.
Whip	a heavier timber 'backbone' supporting the lighter timber framing of the sail.
Wind, to	*see* weather, to
Wind shaft	the near horizontal shaft of either wood or metal carrying the sails and brake wheel.
Wire machine	a rotary sifting device, the sifting medium being a stationary wire mesh cylinder swept internally by revolving brushes—*see* bolter.

BIBLIOGRAPHY

W. G. Hoskins, *The Making of the English Landscape* (Hodder, 1970).
Rev. Giles, *The History of Witney . . . of Bampton.*
F. S. Thacker, *The Thames Highway* (David & Charles, reprint, 1968).
Anthony Wood, *The City of Oxford.*
T. W. Squires, *In West Oxford* (Mowbray, 1928).
W. H. Turner, *Records of the City of Oxford* (Parker, 1880).
Alfred Shorter, *Paper Making in the British Isles* (David & Charles, 1971).
Victoria County Histories of Oxfordshire and Berkshire.
Plumm and Early, *The Blanket Makers* (Routlidge, Kegan, Paul, 1969).
Voller, *Modern Flour Milling* (1897).
John Reynolds, *Windmills and Watermills* (Hugh Evelyn, 1970).
Rex Wailes, *The English Windmill.*
Rex Wailes, *Windmills of England.*
Stanley Freese, *Mills and Millwrighting* (David & Charles, 1957).
Coles Finch, *Watermills and Windmills* (Cassell. Sheerness, 1976).
J. Kenneth Major, *Berkshire Watermills.*
Bennett and Elton, *The History of Corn Milling* (1898).
P. Harvey, *The Mediaeval Oxfordshire Village* (O.U.P., 1965).
Percy Rushen, *Old Time Inventions of the Four Shires* (Oxford City Library).
Industrial Archaeology of Water Wheels and Water Power, No. 11 (Heinemann, Educational Books, Ltd.).
J. Allen and R. Bird, *Energy Paper No. 21* (H.M.S.O., 1978).
Arthur Smith, *Windmills in Bucks. and Oxon.* (Stevenage Museum).
Jean Gimpel, *The Medieval Machine* (Holt, Rinehart and Winsten 1980).
J. Kenneth Major, *Animal Powered Engines* (Batsford, 1978).
The Simmons Papers available at the Science Museum Library, London
Various other S.P.A.B. publications and Transactions of the Newcomen Society as available.

INDEX

LIST OF SUBSCRIBERS

A. M. Abbott
Malcolm Airs
Julian C. Allen
John Ashdown
Michael Aston
F. R. S. Atkins
Jonathan Aylen
N. J. Bacon
L. E. Ball
Peter G. Ball
A. E. Bancroft
R. Barltrop
Mr. B. V. Barton
J. A. Bedington
John P. Bicknell
S. H. Biellik
B. G. Birdseye
Tony Stuart Blay
Simon and Judy Bocock
C. J. Bond
D. T. N. Booth
Mr. R. A. Breeze
Geoffrey Charles Bridger
Peter J. S. Brooks
Mrs. M. A. Brown
M. Brunnarius
Hugo Brunner
A. A. Bryan
D. W. Burrage
Nicholas Catford
R. A. Chambers
Desmond H. Codd
Mildred Cookson
Dennis W. Coombs
Eric Cooper
Madeline Cornish
Terence E. Crowley
B. J. Darlow
Rosemary A. Dennis
Mrs. J. Edmonds
D. G. Fallowfield
K. G. Farries
Mrs. K. P. Fisher
Brian Flint
John G. Francis
Michael J. Fuller
Alan F. Gifford
Robert J. Girling
John Godfrey

Edith Gollnast
John Goodacre
Bishop Eric Gordon
Francois Gordon
Gerald J. Gracey-Cox
R. W. Grant
Dave Gregory
F. W. Gregory
Roy Gregory
Mike Hallam-Wootton
F. W. Hamond
Mrs. A. Hancock
E. J. Handy
Tom Hassall
Mr. A. E. Hemmings
A. R. Heygate
Peter J. Hill
K. R. & A. E. Hirons
Christopher Hohler
K. Martin Horswell
M. S. Howlett
Barry Hudson
Chris Hullcoop
P. S. Jarvis
Alex Jenkins
Miss R. L. Jenkins
Peter Jennings
Barry Job
Ruth H. C. Johnson
Alun T. Jones
Lyndon & Daphne Jones
Catherine Kirkwood
G. H. Lambrick
Elizabeth Leggatt
Adrian Lewis
Edward Loft
C. L. Lovell
Cliff & Marguerite Lovett
R. A. Lowe
J. Kenneth Major
Roger Mant
Nigel J. T. Melican
N. J. Merrow-Smith
The Library, Merton College,
    Oxford
Lord Miles of Blackfriars
Mr. & Mrs. R. Moody
Graham Moore
D. Morton

Donald W. Muggeridge
Rodney Newall
Oxfordshire County Record
    Office
Oxfordshire Museum Services
Roger Parker, M.S., F.R.C.S.
Miss R. Pasco
Don Paterson
Ian John Pelling
G. M. Percival
Emma Perrin
Andrew Pitt
Douglas F. Pluck, F.R.I.C.S.
Don Porter
J. D. Reynolds
Clyde T. Riley
Niall Roberts
Giles Robinson
Mrs. Eva M. Coram Sale
Wilfred A. Seaby
R. W. Shadbolt
Stuart Silvester
B. J. Simpson
Arthur C. Smith
J. H. Spencer
Alan Stoyel
G. E. Summersby
Andrew J. Taylor
Jeremy Tilston
S. G. Tooth
Gordon Tucker
J. H. Venn
Mrs. Janice R. Waggott
Wallingford Museum
C. L. Wallis
G. J. O. Wallis
Wantage Museum Committee
David J. Watts, M.Phil.
Martin Watts
Anthony R. Welford
William Henry Wenman
Timothy J. R. Whiskard
Robert Wilkins
Philip Willison
Graham C. Wilson
Bertram Cecil Wood
Brian R. Young
Symon Peter Young